Acknowledgements

Thanks are due to the members of Heriot-Watt University's SCHOLAR team who planned and created these materials, and to the many colleagues who reviewed the content.

We would like to acknowledge the assistance of the education authorities, colleges, teachers and students who contributed to the SCHOLAR programme and who evaluated these materials.

Grateful acknowledgement is made for permission to use the following material in the SCHOLAR programme:

The Scottish Qualifications Authority for permission to use Past Papers assessments.

The Scottish Government for financial support.

The content of this Study Guide is aligned to the Scottish Qualifications Authority (SQA) curriculum.

All brand names, product names, logos and related devices are used for identification purposes only and are trademarks, registered trademarks or service marks of their respective holders.

SCHOLAR Study Guide

CfE Advanced Higher Biology
Unit 1: Cells and Proteins

Authored by:

Bryony Smith (North Berwick High School)

Dawn Campbell (Falkirk High School)

Reviewed by:

Fiona Stewart (Perth Grammar School)

Previously authored by:

Jaquie Burt

Lorraine Knight

Eileen Humphrey

Nadine Randle

Heriot-Watt University

Edinburgh EH14 4AS, United Kingdom.

First published 2015 by Heriot-Watt University.

This edition published in 2015 by Heriot-Watt University SCHOLAR.

Copyright © 2015 SCHOLAR Forum.

Members of the SCHOLAR Forum may reproduce this publication in whole or in part for educational purposes within their establishment providing that no profit accrues at any stage, Any other use of the materials is governed by the general copyright statement that follows.

All rights reserved. No part of this publication may be reproduced, stored in a retrieval system or transmitted in any form or by any means, without written permission from the publisher.

Heriot-Watt University accepts no responsibility or liability whatsoever with regard to the information contained in this study guide.

Distributed by the SCHOLAR Forum.

SCHOLAR Study Guide Unit 1: CfE Advanced Higher Biology

1. CfE Advanced Higher Biology Course Code: C707 77

ISBN 978-1-909633-60-5

Print Production and fulfilment in UK by Print Trail www.printtrail.com

Contents

Topic 1

Laboratory techniques for biologists

Contents

Prerequisite knowledge

You should already know that:

- *an example of aseptic technique is wearing a lab coat;*

- *growth media can be composed of specific substances or can contain complex ingredients such as beef extract;*

- *culture conditions include sterility (to eliminate any effects of contaminating microorganisms), control of temperature, control of oxygen levels by aeration, and control of pH by buffers or the addition of acid or alkali.*

Learning objectives

By the end of this topic, you should be able to:

- *explain how to identify and control hazards and assess risk in a lab environment;*

- *state that chemicals or organisms can be intrinsically hazardous and that their use may involve risks to people, to other organisms or to the environment;*

- *describe the use of physical control measures, such as personal protective equipment and biological control, for example using a more suitable strain of microorganism e.g. less virulent;*

- *describe how to carry out a dilution series;*

- *describe how unknown concentrations can be determined;*

- *explain the role of buffers in maintaining and controlling pH;*

- *describe the use of cylinders, pipettes, burettes, autopipettors and syringes;*

- *state that pH can be measured using a meter or an indicator;*

- *state that the concentration of a pigmented compound can be quantified using a colorimeter;*

- *state that substances can be separated according to their solubility, size, shape or charge;*

- *describe the process of centrifugation;*

- *describe the use of paper, thin layer and affinity chromatography;*

- *state that protein electrophoresis uses current flowing through a buffer to separate proteins;*

- *state that proteins can be separated using pH - at their iso-electric point they have an overall neutral charge and precipitate out of solution;*

- *state that antibody techniques can be used for the detection and identification of specific proteins;*

- *state that immunoassay techniques use antibodies linked to reporter enzymes to cause a colour change in the presence of a specific antigen;*

- *describe the use of labelled antibodies in blotting and immunohistochemical staining of tissue;*

- *describe the creation of monoclonal antibodies;*

- *describe the use of bright field and fluorescence microscopy;*

- *describe the use of haemocytometers;*

- *describe the use of flow cytometry;*

- *explain how estimates of viable and total cell counts can be made;*

- *describe the difference between the lifetime of primary cells lines compared to cancer cell lines;*

- *state that culture media contain requirements of the cells;*

- *explain the need for complex media containing growth factors from serum for animal cell culture;*

- *describe the importance of aseptic technique and give some examples.*

1.1   Health and safety

You will be familiar with health and safety rules from working in a school laboratory. Many biological laboratory health and safety rules are similar to those in a school laboratory and most are common sense. For example, safety glasses/goggles should be worn at all times while working with chemicals, heat or glassware to protect the eyes from potential harm.

The following table details some health and safety issues which have arisen in research laboratories and the recommended health and safety actions which should be put in place to minimise potential harm.

Concern statement	Health and safety recommended actions
Two scientists working in a laboratory experienced health and safety issues relating to liquid nitrogen. The main hazard related to working with liquid nitrogen is extremely low temperatures (in the order of -200 °C or lower), which can lead to tissue damage. The first incident involved an employee filling a four litre bottle with liquid nitrogen. After stopping the flow of liquid nitrogen to check how full the bottle was, the researcher opened the liquid flow valve to continue filling. Restarting the flow of liquid nitrogen resulted in liquid nitrogen splashing out of the bottle and onto her hand. In a second case, a researcher received first and second degree contact burns to his left hand when he tried to shut the liquid flow valve on a 200 litre liquid nitrogen bottle.	Researchers and staff should be reminded of the importance of appropriate personal protective equipment. For example, when handling liquid nitrogen, appropriate eye protection includes safety glasses with side shields (if working with small volumes of liquid nitrogen), and safety glasses with side shields and a face shield (if working with liquid nitrogen from a pressurised line). Insulated gloves should be worn at all times to protect against extremely low temperatures. Good lab practice, such as wearing closed-toe shoes, trousers (not shorts or skirts) and a lab coat, is also required.
A centrifuge spins samples at high speed to separate out the components. A lab was running a centrifuge containing milk samples, which were placed in the rotor section. The rotor holds individual sample tubes and is connected to the spin drive of the centrifuge. Halfway through the procedure, the rotor failed due to excessive mechanical stress; this caused an explosion which destroyed the centrifuge. The safety shielding on the centrifuge failed and fragments of the centrifuge, including the steel rotor, were ejected from the machine. Metal fragments made holes in the walls and ceilings, and four windows were shattered due to the shockwave created by the explosion. Although the room was severely damaged, it was unoccupied at the time of the explosion and no injuries were reported. The explosion was caused by the use of an incorrect rotor in the centrifuge.	The rotor in a centrifuge is spun at extremely high speed and this causes powerful mechanical stress that can cause the rotor to fail. A centrifuge must be loaded correctly or the rotor may break loose while spinning. All researchers using a centrifuge must be aware of the proper operating procedures, including how to select, load, balance and clean the rotor. Laboratory supervisors are responsible for ensuring that all researchers are properly trained and that equipment is well maintained. If equipment is checked and there are signs of wear or damage to rotors, the equipment should be taken out of service immediately and clearly marked "Warning - do not use" until checked by an authorised service technician.

Concern statement	Health and safety recommended actions
Recently, in a research lab, five persons required medical treatment for cuts sustained from broken glassware within a six month period.	All laboratories must have a formal plan for handling glassware, which should be stored in a safe place. Safe working areas should be provided for all work with glassware, i.e. glassware washing areas should have lots of clear space, sufficient safe drying racks and safe glassware storage areas. Appropriate gloves should be worn, i.e. slip resistant. Glassware should be regularly inspected, and broken, cracked or chipped items should be discarded. All researchers should be aware of proper procedures for disposal of broken glass.
Whilst operating a UV transilluminator, a researcher failed to wear the appropriate personal protective equipment (PPE). After using the transilluminator multiple times over a one hour period, the researcher suffered reddening of the skin and temporary eye injury resulting from UV exposure to her face and eyes.	A UV transilluminator emits UV light at intensities many times greater than the summer midday sun. Therefore, it can cause severe damage to the skin and eyes, even when standing several feet away. The light box shield must be kept in place at all times. Appropriate personal protective equipment must be used when working with a UV light source, including a face shield, safety glasses, gloves and a fully buttoned lab coat. All researchers must be made aware of the safe use of a UV transilluminator.

Chemicals or organisms can be intrinsically hazardous. Their use may involve risks to people, to other organisms or to the environment. Risk assessments must be performed when using certain substances in a laboratory. Control of substances hazardous to health (COSHH) regulations cover substances that are hazardous to health, as the name implies, including:

- chemicals;

- products containing chemicals;

- fumes;

- dusts;

- vapours and mists;

- nanotechnology;

- gases and asphyxiating gases;

- biological agents.

A COSHH assessment form allows a risk assessment to be carried out for any substance which is potentially hazardous. In this form, factors such as exposure, disposal procedures and handling procedures are considered. Follow the link to view a COSHH assessment form: http://www.hse.gov.uk/nanotechnology/coss-assessment-form.doc

One of the most important aspects of health and safety is personal protective equipment (PPE), which reduces the risk of hazardous materials coming into contact with the skin where it could cause harm.

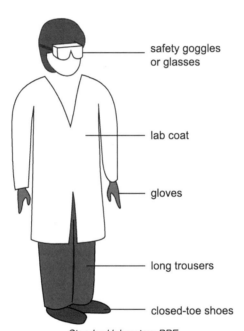

safety goggles
or glasses

lab coat

gloves

long trousers

closed-toe shoes

Standard laboratory PPE

Many biology laboratories work with living organisms. Living organisms can pose potential harm to the health and safety of people working in the laboratory, and the environment, therefore procedures must be put in place to minimise risk. For example, researchers working with microorganisms must follow stringent guidelines to ensure not only their own health and safety, but also that of others working in the laboratory, whilst additionally protecting the environment. Living organisms, such as microorganisms, can be controlled by biological means, for example by using a more suitable, e.g. less virulent, strain of microorganism. Genetically modified (GM) microorganisms may have genes introduced which prevent their survival outside the laboratory. This helps to avoid environmental contamination if the microorganism escapes the laboratory.

1.2   Liquids and solutions

Measuring liquids

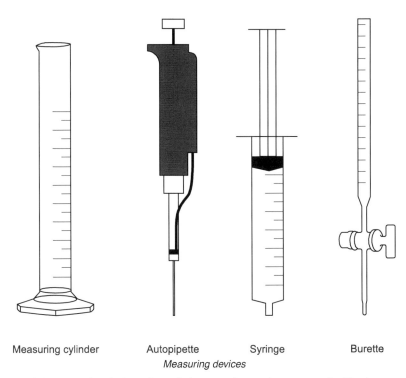

Measuring cylinder   Autopipette   Syringe   Burette

Measuring devices

All of the measuring devices pictured above can be used to measure liquid volumes. You are probably familiar with the use of measuring cylinders and syringes, but you may not have come across autopipettors or burettes in biology before.

An autopipette allows small volumes of liquid to be measured very accurately. The autopipette is first set to the desired volume within its range and a disposable plastic tip is placed on the end. The plunger at the top of an autopipette has two stops. To draw liquid into the autopipette, the plunger is pressed down to the first stop, the tip is placed just under the surface of the liquid and the plunger is released. This draws the desired volume of liquid into the tip. To pipette the liquid into a new tube, the tip is placed against the side of the tube and the plunger is pressed down beyond the first stop to the second stop. This second stop ensures that all the liquid from the tip is released.

Burettes are used to dispense precise volumes of liquid reagents. The burette is rinsed with the solution to be used by filling it, then opening the tap at the bottom and allowing the solution to run through. The tap is closed and the burette is filled to just above the 0 cm^3 mark with the required solution. The tap is then slowly opened and the solution is run down to the 0 cm^3 mark. The tap is closed and the burette is ready for use.

When measuring from a burette, it is important to take readings from the bottom of the meniscus. The meniscus is the curved top surface of the liquid inside the burette. This is shown in the following image (where the correct reading is 20 cm^3).

Meniscus in a burette by PRHaney, licenced under the Creative Commons http://creativ ecommons.org/licenses/by-sa/3.0/deed.en license

Burettes are often used in titration experiments which require solution of a known concentration to be used to determine the concentration of an unknown solution.

Dilution series

Serial dilutions are an important laboratory technique. Dilution involves reducing the concentration of a substance in a solution. Repeated dilution from a stock solution is known as a serial dilution.

The following diagram demonstrates how a serial dilution can be performed. 1 cm^3 of the stock solution is transferred to a new tube and 9 cm^3 of water is added to produce a concentration of 10^{-1}. To produce a concentration of 10^{-2}, 1 cm^3 of the 10^{-1} solution is removed and placed in a new tube and 9 cm^3 of water is added. This process is repeated until the lowest required concentration has been produced. Each step is a tenfold dilution; therefore, this is an example of a logarithmic dilution.

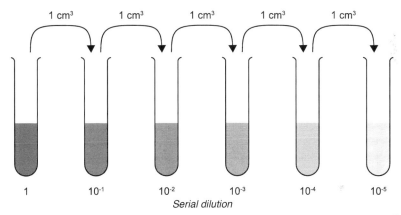

Serial dilution

Serial dilutions are widely performed in microbiology. For example, an investigator may need to know the number of bacterial cells which are contained within an environmental sample. It is likely that there are too many cells in the sample to physically count every one; therefore, we can carry out a dilution series. A dilution series allows the scientist to dilute the original concentration of bacteria in a stepwise manner. A sample from each dilution can be added to an agar plate and incubated until colonies develop. The investigator will select a plate with a countable number of colonies (usually between 30 and 300). By counting the number of colonies on a plate and knowing the concentration of the solution, the investigator can assess the number of cells per cm^3 in the original culture.

Colorimeter

The concentration of a pigmented compound can be quantified using a **colorimeter**. A colorimeter measures the absorbance of specific wavelengths of light by a solution. A colorimeter works by passing a light beam, at a specific wavelength, through a cuvette containing a sample solution. Some of the light is absorbed by the sample; therefore, light of a lower intensity hits the detector and the machine will display an absorbance value.

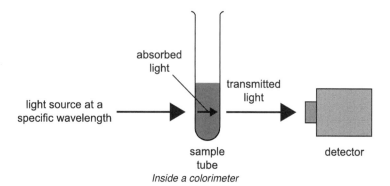

Inside a colorimeter

To use a colorimeter, the correct wavelength of light must first be selected (directions for most colorimetry experiments usually give a recommended wavelength) and the machine must be calibrated. To calibrate a colorimeter, a cuvette containing calibration solution (usually distilled water) is placed in the cuvette compartment and the calibrate button is pressed. This will provide the user with a reading of 0 absorbance. The user can then place a cuvette containing a sample solution into the cuvette compartment and take a reading of the absorbance of the sample by pressing the test button.

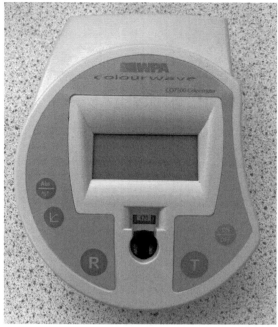

A colorimeter

pH of solutions

pH is a measure of the acidity or basicity of a solution. Acidic solutions have a pH of less than 7 and basic (or alkaline) solutions have a pH of greater than 7. A solution with a pH of 7 is said to be neutral. pH is a logarithmic measure of hydrogen ion concentration.

$$pH = -\log\left[H^+\right]$$

The pH of a solution can be measured using an electronic meter or an indicator.

pH	Examples of solutions
0	Battery acid, strong hydrofluoric acid
1	Hydrochloric acid secreted by stomach lining
2	Lemon juice, gastric acid, vinegar
3	Grapefruit juice, orange juice, soda
4	Tomato juice, acid rain
5	Soft drinking water, black coffee
6	Urine, saliva
7	'Pure' water
8	Sea water
9	Baking soda
10	Great Salt Lake, milk of magnesia
11	Ammonia solution
12	Soapy water
13	Bleach, oven cleaner
14	Liquid drain cleaner

pH scale

A pH buffer is a solution whose pH changes very little when a small amount of acid or base is added to it. Buffers work by allowing the addition of hydrogen or hydroxide ions without affecting the pH of the solution. Buffer solutions are used as a means of keeping pH at a nearly constant value. A buffer of carbonic acid and bicarbonate is present in blood plasma to maintain a pH between 7.35 and 7.45.

Determining an unknown concentration

It can often be important to determine unknown concentrations of solutions in a laboratory. A **standard curve** is one method that is used to determine the concentration of a solution. A series of 'standards' of known concentration are measured and graphed. This graph can then be used to determine the concentration of an unknown sample.

One such example is the Bradford protein assay. In this test, the depth of colour produced by coomassie brilliant blue dye changes depending on the concentration of protein in the sample; this can be measured using a colorimeter.

© HERIOT-WATT UNIVERSITY

To produce a standard curve, coomassie brilliant blue dye is added to known concentrations of protein solutions. The ideal protein solution to use is a purified preparation of the unknown sample; however, this may not always be available. In the absence of purified preparations of the protein being analysed, protein standards may be used. The two most common protein standards used are BSA and gamma-globulin. The absorbance of each known protein solution is measured using a colorimeter with a filter at 595 nm. The absorbance of each solution can then be plotted on a graph with the concentration on one axis and the absorbance on the other, producing a standard curve. The same dye (coomassie brilliant blue) is added to the protein sample of unknown concentration and an absorbance reading is taken. The standard curve can then be used to determine the concentration of protein in the sample based on its absorbance.

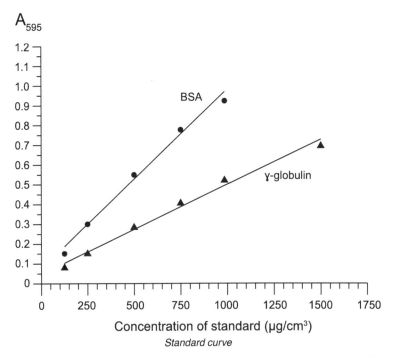

Standard curve

Another method used to determine the concentration of an unknown solution is a titration. Titrations are carried out using a burette to deliver a solution of known volume and concentration to a solution of unknown concentration underneath. The volume and concentration of the known solution along with the stoichiometry of the reaction are used to calculate the concentration of the unknown solution.

© HERIOT-WATT UNIVERSITY

1.3 Separation techniques

Substances can be separated according to their solubility, size, shape or charge. The techniques we will look at are:

- **centrifugation**;
- protein **electrophoresis**;
- iso-electric point;
- paper, thin layer and affinity **chromatography**.

Centrifugation

A centrifuge is a piece of equipment that spins a sample at high speed.

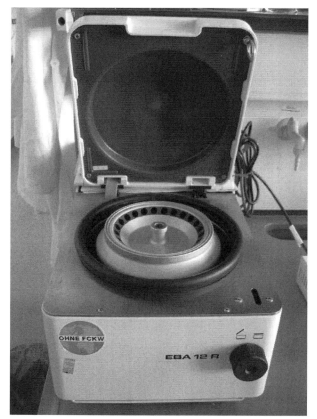

A benchtop centrifuge by http://commons.wikimedia.org/wiki/User:Magnus_Manske, licenced under the Creative Commons http://creativecommons.org/licenses/by/1.0/dee d.en license

© HERIOT-WATT UNIVERSITY

Centrifugation allows substances to be separated according to their size and density. The largest and densest materials separate out first and form a pellet at the bottom of the tube. The liquid which remains above the pellet is called the supernatant.

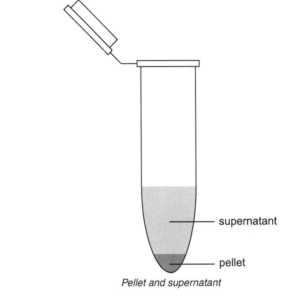

Pellet and supernatant

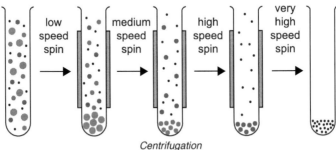

Centrifugation

A centrifuge can spin at extremely high speeds (up to 70,000 rpm for ultracentrifuges) which means that it must be carefully operated to avoid health and safety issues. For example, it is important to ensure that the tubes are balanced; this means that the samples placed into a centrifuge should hold a similar volume and should be placed in the rotor at opposite sides.

Protein electrophoresis

Proteins can be separated by gel electrophoresis. This process separates proteins based upon their charge and/or size/shape. Protein electrophoresis uses current flowing through a buffer to separate proteins. The gel used in protein electrophoresis acts as a sieve, separating the proteins. One form of protein electrophoresis is SDS-PAGE. During this procedure, the proteins are denatured and given a uniform negative charge; this means that the proteins can be separated based on their size as they migrate towards the positive electrode. Small proteins travel further through the gel than large proteins.

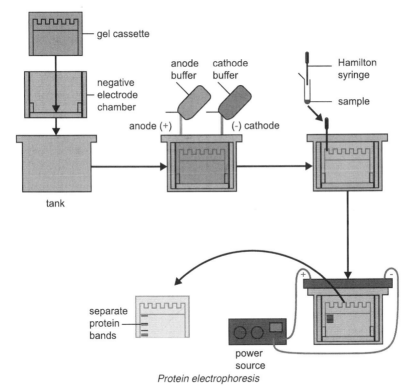

Protein electrophoresis

It is also possible to run native gels where the protein is not denatured before the gel electrophoresis. This allows the scientist to analyse the proteins in their folded state. In this case, the migration of the proteins through the gel depends on the protein charge and shape.

© HERIOT-WATT UNIVERSITY

Iso-electric point

Proteins can be separated using their pH. At their iso-electric point, they have an overall neutral charge and precipitate out of solution.

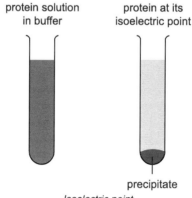

Isoelectric point

Proteins are made up of amino acids which may carry a positive, negative or neutral charge. The combined charges of the amino acids in a protein give the protein its overall charge. The charge of a protein will vary depending on the pH of the solution it is in. At their iso-electric point, proteins have an overall neutral charge. Proteins carry an overall positive charge at a pH below their isoelectric point and a negative charge at a pH above their isoelectric point. Isoelectric focussing uses a pH gradient to separate proteins according to their isoelectric point.

In isoelectric focussing, a pH gradient is set up along a tube of polyacrylamide gel using a mixture of special buffers. Each protein in the sample that is loaded onto the gel will move until it reaches the pH corresponding to its isoelectric point. At this pH, the protein will move no further and form a band which can be visualised after staining.

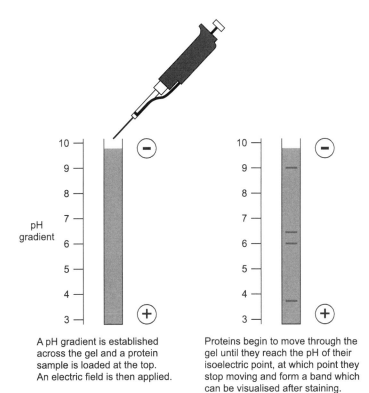

A pH gradient is established across the gel and a protein sample is loaded at the top. An electric field is then applied.

Proteins begin to move through the gel until they reach the pH of their isoelectric point, at which point they stop moving and form a band which can be visualised after staining.

Isoelectric focussing

Paper, thin layer and affinity chromatography

Chromatography refers to a set of techniques which separates the components of a mixture. Chromatography allows scientists to identify and (in some types of chromatography) purify the components of a mixture. Chromatography can be used to separate mixtures of amino acids and proteins. The mixture is dissolved in a fluid known as the mobile phase. The components of the mixture are separated as they pass through a stationary phase, which varies depending on the type of chromatography being used.

In paper chromatography, the stationary phase is a strip of chromatography paper. A sample of the mixture being separated is placed in a dot, or line, near the bottom of a strip of chromatography paper which is then placed in a solvent. The solvent moves up through the chromatography paper and carries the components of the mixture with it, which will travel at different rates depending on their properties. For example, paper contains cellulose fibres which are polar in nature; any components of the mixture which are polar will bond with the cellulose fibres relatively quickly and do not travel far up the paper. Non-polar components of the mixture will not bind as readily to the paper and travel further.

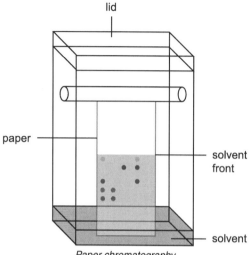

Paper chromatography

Thin layer chromatography (TLC) is similar to paper chromatography, but the stationary phase differs. Rather than using a stationary phase of chromatography paper, TLC uses a strip of absorbent material, such as silica gel, on a non-reactive backing. The rest of the process works in a similar manner to paper chromatography where a solvent moves up through the stationary phase and carries the components of the mixture with it. Again, the components will travel different distances depending on how soluble they are in the solvent and how much they bind to the stationary phase.

The process of affinity chromatography differs from paper and thin layer chromatography. Affinity chromatography relies on the binding interactions between a protein and ligand. A ligand is immobilised on an inert support in a column and a protein mixture is passed through the column. The protein, which is complementary to the ligand in the column, will bind to it and remain in the column when the other components are washed away. The target protein can then be stripped from the support, resulting in its separation and purification from the original sample.

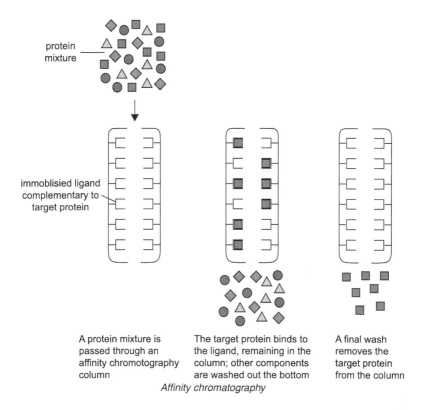

A protein mixture is passed through an affinity chromotography column

The target protein binds to the ligand, remaining in the column; other components are washed out the bottom

A final wash removes the target protein from the column

Affinity chromatography

1.4   Antibody techniques

Immunoassay

Antibodies play an important role within the immune system, identifying foreign proteins (antigens) and flagging them for destruction.   Scientists have learned to produce antibodies and use them in the detection and identification of proteins.

Antibodies can be used to detect both the presence and concentration of a protein within a solution. This type of biochemical test is called an **immunoassay** and relies on the specificity of antibodies; in other words, their ability to recognise and bind with only one antigen. Any antibody used in an immunoassay must be linked to a detectable label to allow scientists to detect when binding has occurred. These labels may be in the form of a reporter enzyme which causes a colour change in the presence of a specific antigen.

The following diagram shows a typical immunoassay: the molecule being detected (a protein) is shown in green, the antibody in grey and the detectable label in yellow.

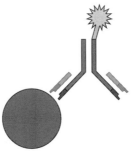

Immunoassay

ELISA (enzyme-linked immunosorbent assay) is an analytical technique which uses antibodies to detect the presence of an antigen within a solution. There are three forms of ELISA: direct, indirect and sandwich.

- During direct ELISA, the antigen is allowed to bind to the surface of a multiwell plate. A primary antibody, linked to a reporter enzyme, is added to the well and binds to the antigen.

- During indirect ELISA, the antigen is allowed to bind to the surface of a multiwell plate. A primary antibody is added to the well and allowed to bind to the antigen. A secondary antibody, linked to a reporter enzyme, is then added, which binds to the primary antibody.

- During sandwich ELISA, a capture antibody is bound to the surface of a multiwell plate. The antigen is added and allowed to bind to the capture antibody. A primary antibody, which binds to the antigen, is added to the well. A secondary antibody, linked to a reporter enzyme, is then added, which binds to the primary antibody.

In each case, a colour-producing substrate is added to the well and a colour is allowed to develop. Any wells which remain colourless indicate a negative result (the protein of interest is not present in that sample), while any wells which show a colour change indicate a positive result (the protein of interest is present in that sample).

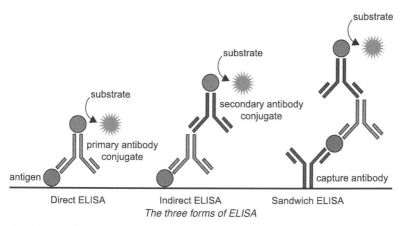

Direct ELISA   Indirect ELISA   Sandwich ELISA
The three forms of ELISA

The following diagram shows results from an ELISA test. Wells which show a colour change (brown) indicate the presence of the antigen of interest. ELISA has found many applications, examples of which include the detection of HIV and food allergens (such as peanuts), and screening for certain types of drugs.

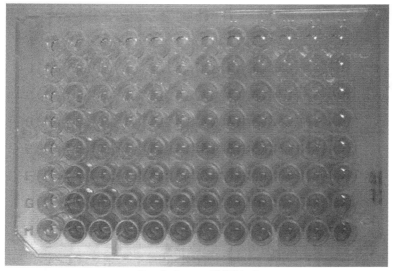

Results from an ELISA test

Protein blotting

Antibodies are also used in a process called protein blotting, which allows protein from a tissue or cell extract to be detected. Proteins from the sample are first separated using gel electrophoresis, after which the proteins are transferred to a membrane.

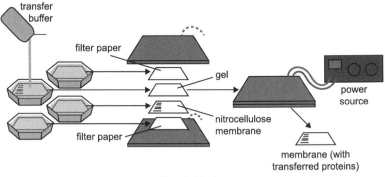

Protein blotting

The membrane is then probed for the protein of interest using a specific antibody that is linked to a detectable label. This label may be a reporter enzyme which brings about a detectable colour change to indicate the presence of the target protein. Protein blotting allows scientists to identify specific proteins which are present in a cell sample, for example if it has medical applications in the diagnosis of HIV and hepatitis B.

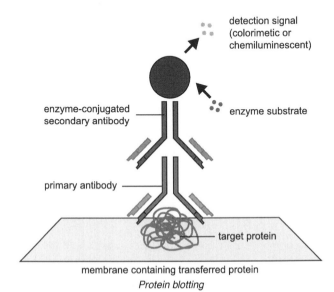

Protein blotting

Immunohistochemistry

Antibodies can be used to detect the presence of a particular antigen within a tissue sample; a process known as immunohistochemistry. This technique is commonly used in the diagnosis of diseases such as cancer because it can identify abnormal gene expression within cells. Samples of tissue are very thinly sliced and mounted onto a slide. The sample is then interrogated for the presence of a particular protein using an enzyme-linked antibody. As with other types of immunoassays, the enzyme brings about a detectable colour change to indicate that the antibody has bound to the target protein. The advantage of immunohistochemistry lies in the fact that it is capable of showing exactly where a certain protein is being expressed within a tissue sample.

The following image shows immunohistochemical staining of a biopsy taken from a brain tumour. The sample was tested for the presence of INI1 protein; this protein is known to be down-regulated in some forms of brain cancer. In the following image, you can see the lack of brown staining in many of the cells, indicating that the tumour is cancerous.

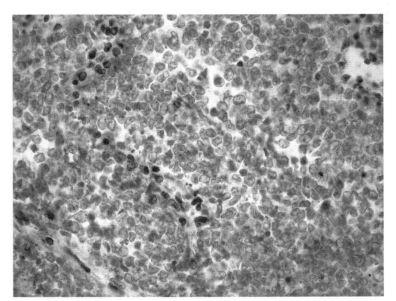

Immunohistochemistry by http://de.wikipedia.org/wiki/User:Marvin_101, licenced under the Creative Commons http://creativecommons.org/licenses/by-sa/2.0/de/deed.en license

Monoclonal antibodies

Scientists have found many uses for antibodies, but they also require methods to make the antibodies which are specific to the protein that they wish to detect. They also need to be able to produce these antibodies in large quantities; to achieve this goal, **hybridomas** are formed by fusion of a B lymphocyte with a **myeloma** cell using polyethylene glycol (PEG).

Laboratory animals, for example mice, are used to produce stocks of monoclonal antibodies. To produce hybridomas, we need to induce the animal to make antibody producing B lymphocytes. This is achieved by exposing the animal to the antigen of interest. Blood tests are carried out on the animal to determine if it is producing antibodies. If the desired antibody is being produced, B lymphocytes are removed from the spleen of the animal and fused with myeloma cells using polyethylene glycol, forming hybridomas.

The cells are then cultured in a special medium called hypoxanthine-aminopterin-thymidine (HAT). Any unfused B lymphocytes die because they are unable to survive in culture while unfused myeloma cells die because they cannot survive in the HAT medium. The hybridomas survive and produce antibodies (a property of B lymphocytes) while also being immortal (a property of myeloma cells).

The surviving hybridomas are diluted and cultured in a multiwell plate. Each well only contains one cell. After culturing for a few weeks, each well contains clones of hybridomas which are producing antibodies. The supernatant (culture medium) in each well can be screened for the desired antibody. Clones which produce the desired antibody are then cultured on a large scale.

mouse challenged with antigen

B lymphocytes   myeloma cells

fusion using PEG

hybridomas

culture in HAT medium   harvest monoclonal
select for positive cells   antibodies

Production of monoclonal antibodies

Production of monoclonal antibodies

Q1: Put the following stages of the production of monoclonal antibodies into the correct order.

Go online

- Individual hybridomas are cultured in a multiwell plate.
- B lymphocytes are removed from the spleen of the animal.
- The culture medium can be removed and screened for the desired antibody.
- Hybridomas which produce the desired antibody are cultured on a large scale.
- B lymphocytes are fused with myeloma cells using polyethylene glycol, forming hybridomas.
- A laboratory animal is exposed to the antigen of interest.

. . . .

1.5 Microscopy

Bright field and fluorescence microscopy

Bright-field microscopy is a relatively simple and straightforward microscopy technique. A sample is mounted on a slide and illuminated from below. Light is transmitted through the specimen to the objective lens (which magnifies the image) and then to the eyepiece at the top of the microscope where the image is observed. The image of the sample that is produced is usually darker than the background which appears bright, hence the name bright field microscopy. Samples are often stained before being viewed using a bright field microscope to increase contrast.

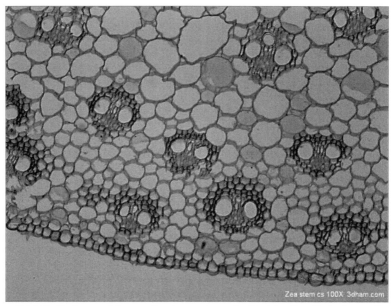

Bright field micrograph image of a stem cross section by John Alan Elson, licenced under the Creative Commons http://creativecommons.org/licenses/by-sa/3.0/deed.en license

Fluorescence microscopy allows particular protein structures to be visualised. A fluorescent molecule is one which absorbs a specific wavelength of light then emits a different (longer) wavelength. This means that it absorbs light of one colour and emits light of a different colour. In fluorescence microscopy, specific protein structures have fluorescent markers added to them. The cells can then be placed on a slide and the protein structure visualised using a fluorescence microscope.

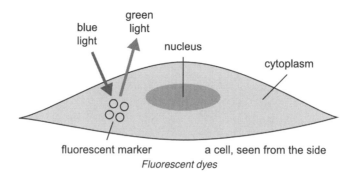

Fluorescent dyes

© HERIOT-WATT UNIVERSITY

In some cases, antibodies are used to fluorescently tag protein structures. This is known as immunofluoresecence. A primary antibody, which is specific to the protein being visualised, is introduced to a cell sample. A secondary antibody, attached to a fluorescent tag, is then added which binds to the primary antibody.

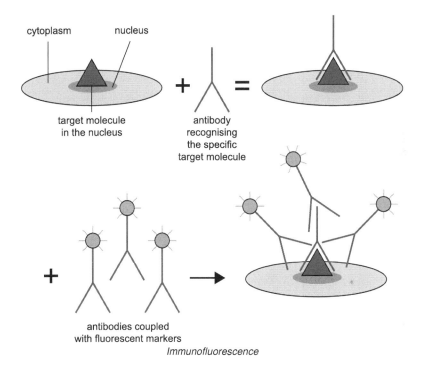

Immunofluorescence

© HERIOT-WATT UNIVERSITY

In a fluorescent microscope, the light passing through the sample first passes through a filter which only lets through light at a specific wavelength that corresponds to the fluorescent marker being used. When this light hits the fluorescent marker, it fluoresces and emits light of a different wavelength. The second filter separates emitted light from the light first passed through the specimen and the fluorescing regions of the sample can be viewed in the microscope.

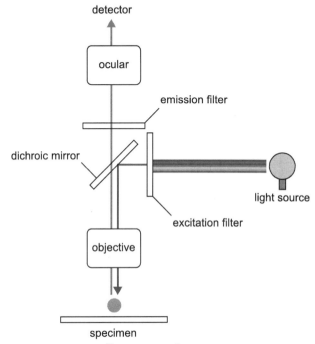

Fluorescence microscopy

The following image shows endothelial cells under a microscope. Nuclei are marked blue, microtubules are marked green and actin filaments are marked red.

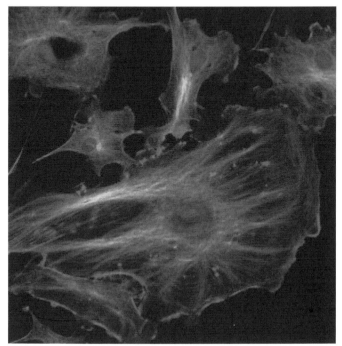

Fluorescent cells

Haemocytometer

A **haemocytometer** allows an estimation of the concentration of cells in a sample to be made. A haemocytometer resembles a microscope slide, but has a grid made up of perpendicular lines (similar to graph paper) etched into the glass.

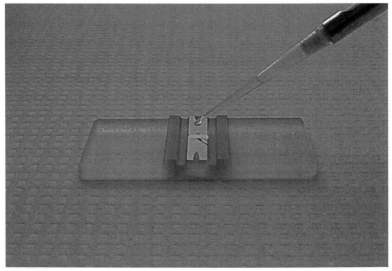

Haemocytometer by http://flickr.com/photos/83788754@N00, licenced under the Creative Commons http://creativecommons.org/licenses/by-sa/2.0/deed.en license

To use the haemocytometer, a cover slide is affixed to it; this creates a chamber with a depth of exactly 0.1 mm. The cell culture to be counted is gently mixed and 100 μl of the sample is mixed with 100 μl of dye. Some of this mixture is pipetted under the coverslip and the haemocytometer is placed under a microscope to visualise the grid. The following diagram shows the grid on a haemocytometer.

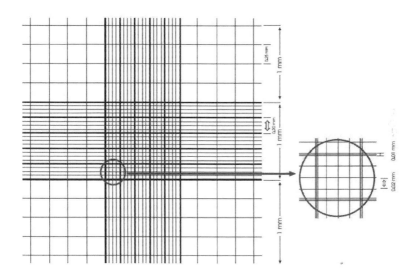

Haemocytometer grid by SantiBadia, licenced under the Creative Commons http://creat ivecommons.org/licenses/by-sa/2.0/deed.en license

The gird has nine 'large' squares, each 1 mm × 1 mm. Using this and the depth under the coverslip (0.1 mm), we can calculate the volume of cell culture in each area of the grid:

$$1 \times 1 \times 0.1 = 0.1 \ mm^3 \text{ (or } 0.1 \ \mu l)$$

The cells within one of the 1 mm × 1 mm areas are visualised using a microscope and counted. This provides an estimate of the number of cells per 0.1 μl of culture medium. Multiplying by 10 gives the number of cells per μl and multiplying by 10,000 gives the number of cells per cm^3. Remember - the cells were diluted in dye as part of this procedure, therefore the final answer should take this into account. A 1:1 dilution gives a dilution factor of 2, therefore the final answer should be multiplied by 2 to give a reliable estimate of cell number per cm^3.

The following diagram shows one of the 1 mm × 1 mm squares of a haemocytometer containing a cell culture sample.

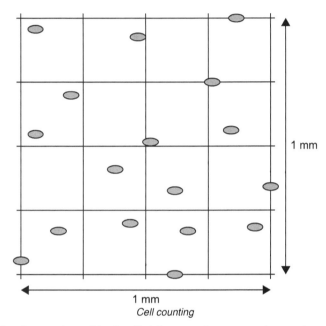

1 mm

1 mm

Cell counting

From the diagram above, it is clear that there may be sources of error when using a haemocytometer to count cells. Should the cells touching the outer boundaries of the area be counted in or not? In general, a rule is set up where, if they are along the top or right border, they are counted, whereas if they are along the left or bottom border, they are not counted. Using the example above, we can estimate the number of cells per cm^3 of culture:

$$15 \; cells \; counted \; \times \; dilution \; factor \; of \; 2 = 30 \; cells \; per \; 0.1 \; \mu l$$
$$30 \times 10 = 300 \; cells \; per \; \mu l$$
$$300 \times 1000 = 300000 \; (3 \times 10^5) \; cells \; per \; cm^3$$

To improve the reliability of the results, the number of cells in more than one square should be counted and an average calculated. When using a traditional glass haemocytometer, the reliability of the results can be effected by incorrect placement of the coverslip because this provides a chamber with a known volume. Many laboratories choose to use plastic disposable haemocytometers which have a coverslip already properly fixed in place, reducing this possible source of error. Disposable haemocytometers also have the added benefit of limiting exposure to infectious materials.

Flow cytometry

Flow cytometry allows scientists to detect, count and analyse cells as they flow past a detector in solution, one by one. As the cells in solution flow through the chamber, they pass a light source (a laser). The passage of the cells interrupts the beam of light and causes it to scatter. The way in which the light bounces off each cell can provide information about its characteristics, for example the cell size. Cells may also be fluorescently labelled and, as they pass the laser, they will emit light which can also be detected. This scattering of light and/or fluorescence is picked up by a detector and converted to electrical signals to allow the type and number of cells in the solution to be ascertained.

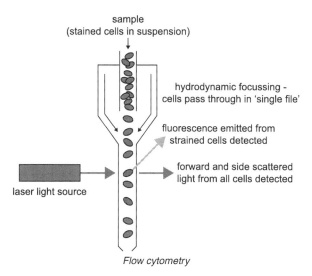

Flow cytometry

1.6 Cell culture and aseptic technique

Cell culture is the ability to grow cells in an artificial laboratory environment. Cell culture is necessary for growing bacterial cells, culturing mammalian cells for cancer studies and many other processes.

Cell culture is often performed in flasks such as those shown in the following image. Cell culture requires environmental factors, for example temperature and pH, to be controlled and the growing cells must be given an opportunity for gas exchange. Both plant and animal cell cultures require complex culture media which contain all the requirements of the cells. Typical culture media contains water, salts (Murashige and Skoog salts for plants), amino acids, vitamins and glucose. Animal cell culture also requires media containing growth factors from serum, for example fetal bovine serum (FBS) which contains growth factors that promote cell proliferation.

Cell culture flask

To perform cell culture, cells must be obtained from a source tissue or culture. The cells that are used to inoculate culture media are called the inoculum. The inoculum may contain cells which have been released from their source tissue using **proteolytic** enzymes or may be explants, which are small pieces of tissue. The inoculum is added to a cell culture flask along with the appropriate growth medium. The cells adhere to the flask and begin to divide. Most cells will only divide a certain number of times and then die. This makes cell culture a challenging procedure for primary cell lines. Cancer cell lines, on the other hand, do not have this limitation, and will grow and divide indefinitely in cell culture.

Aseptic techniques are a vital part of successful cell culture. Aseptic techniques aim to keep cell culture free from contamination by microorganisms such as bacteria. Within all laboratory environments, there are many potential sources of contamination, for example non-sterile media and implements, airborne microorganisms and unclean work surfaces. There are many essential aspects to aseptic techniques which are detailed as follows.

Sterile work area

It is important to ensure that cell culture is performed in a sterile area. To achieve this, cell culture is often performed in culture hoods as shown in the following image. Surfaces are also disinfected before and after use with 70% ethanol or Virkon (a disinfectant).

Cell culture hood

Good personal hygiene

When performing cell culture, hands should be washed before and after all procedures. Appropriate personal protective equipment (PPE) should also be worn, for example a lab coat. This helps to avoid contaminants from the skin and clothes contaminating the cell culture. Gloves should also be worn and any cuts should be covered with a plaster.

Sterile reagents and media

It is important to ensure that all culture media and reagents are free from contaminants. Laboratories use commercial reagents and media which are sterilised as part of their production. They may need to be sterilised again once they have been handled in the laboratory, for example by using an autoclave which is a piece of equipment used to sterilise equipment and other supplies. The object to be sterilised is placed in the chamber of the autoclave and exposed to high pressure and temperature.

Sterile handling

As well as wiping surfaces with ethanol, containers, dishes and flasks should also be wiped down. All reagents should be exposed to the air for as short a period of time as possible, for example by replacing bottle lids swiftly. All pipettes which are used to transfer liquids are either sterile glass or single use disposable plastic. Experiments should be performed as quickly as possible to avoid the potential for entry of contaminants.

Scientists often want to know how many cells are contained within a cell culture flask. A haemocytometer can be used to provide an estimate of both the total and the viable cell number. A viable cell count identifies the number of actively growing/dividing cells in a sample. The haemocytometer is set up using cells stained with trypan blue dye, which is taken up by dead cells but not by living cells. A live cell count can then be performed where only unstained cells are counted. A total cell count is performed by counting all of the cells, including those stained with trypan blue. The percentage viability of a sample can be calculated using the following formula:

$$\frac{\text{Live cell count}}{\text{Total cell count}} = \text{Percentage viability}$$

$$\text{e.g. } \frac{45 \times 10^4 \text{ ml}}{46 \times 10^4 \text{ ml}} = 97.8\% \text{ viability}$$

1.7   Learning points

Summary

- Chemicals or organisms can be intrinsically hazardous and their use may involve risks to people, to other organisms or to the environment.

- Physical control measures include personal protective equipment (PPE), e.g. a lab coat and safety glasses.

- Biological control includes using a more suitable strain of microorganism, e.g. less virulent.

- A dilution series is a stepwise dilution of a stock solution, often performed by diluting 1 cm^3 of solution with 9 cm^3 of water and then repeating the process with the newly produced solution.

- To determine the concentration of an unknown solution, a standard curve can be used. A series of 'standards' of known concentration are measured and graphed. This graph can then be used to determine the concentration of an unknown sample.

- A pH buffer is a solution whose pH changes very little when a small amount of strong acid or base is added to it.

- Cylinders, pipettes, burettes, autopipettors and syringes can all be used to measure liquid volumes.

- pH can be measured using a meter or an indicator.

- The concentration of a pigmented compound can be quantified using a colorimeter.

- Substances can be separated according to their solubility, size, shape or charge.

- Centrifugation allows substances to be separated according to their size and density. The largest and densest materials separate out first and form a pellet at the bottom of the tube. The liquid which remains above the pellet is called the supernatant.

- Chromatography refers to a set of techniques that separate the components of a mixture, including:

    ○ paper chromatography, which separates components using a solvent drawn up a piece of chromatography paper;

    ○ thin layer chromatography, which uses a TLC strip;

    ○ affinity chromatography, which relies on binding interactions between the protein of interest and a ligand.

- Protein electrophoresis uses current flowing through a buffer to separate proteins.

Summary continued

- Proteins can be separated using pH; at their iso-electric point they have an overall neutral charge and precipitate out of solution.

- Antibody techniques can be used for the detection and identification of specific proteins.

- Immunoassay techniques use antibodies that are linked to reporter enzymes to cause a colour change in the presence of a specific antigen.

- Antibodies are used in a process called protein blotting. Proteins are separated and transferred to a membrane which is probed for the protein of interest using a specific antibody that is linked to a detectable label. This label may be a reporter enzyme which brings about a detectable colour change to indicate the presence of the target protein.

- Antibodies are used to detect the presence of a particular protein antigen within a tissue sample, a process known as immunohistochemistry.

- To produce stocks of a particular antibody, hybridomas are formed by fusion of a B lymphocyte with a myeloma cell using polyethylene glycol (PEG).

- Bright field microscopy uses light that is transmitted through a specimen to an objective lens (which magnifies the image) and then to the eyepiece at the top of the microscope where the image is observed.

- Fluorescence microscopy allows particular protein structures to be visualised. Specific protein structures have fluorescent markers added to them. The cells are placed on a slide and the protein structure is visualised using a fluorescence microscope.

- A haemocytometer resembles a microscope slide, but has a grid made up of perpendicular lines etched into the glass. A known volume of cell culture is added to the haemocytometer which is viewed under a microscope to perform cell counts to estimate the number of cells in a sample.

- Flow cytometry allows scientists to detect, count and analyse cells one by one as they flow past a detector in solution.

- Estimates of viable and total cell counts can be made can be made using trypan blue dye, which is absorbed by dead cells. A haemocytometer can then be used to estimate both the total number of cells in culture and the number of viable cells.

- Primary cell lines have a limited lifetime compared to cancer cell lines which will grow and divide indefinitely in cell culture.

- Culture media contain requirements of the cells.

- Complex culture media containing growth factors from serum is required for animal cell culture.

Summary continued

- Aseptic technique aims to keep cell culture free from contamination by microorganisms such as bacteria; examples include sterilisation of equipment, containers and materials, disinfection of the working area and wearing a lab coat.

1.8 End of topic test

End of Topic 1 test

A scientist working in a laboratory was carrying out a DNA gel electrophoresis and used ethidium bromide as a fluorescent tag to visualise the separated DNA. In order to make the ethidium bromide fluoresce and highlight the DNA bands, the gel was placed under UV light.

Go online

Read the following information about ethidium bromide.

Hazards

Ethidium bromide is strongly mutagenic. Ethidium bromide must also be considered a possible carcinogen and reproductive toxin. Therefore all individuals should regularly review their risk assessments and work practices for ethidium bromide. Ethidium bromide is readily absorbed through the skin. Ethidium bromide is highly toxic by inhalation, particularly in powder form, and is irritating to the skin, eyes, mucous membranes and upper respiratory tract.

Q2: Based on the information above, suggest two precautions which should be put in place when working with ethidium bromide. *(2 marks)*

....

Q3: UV light can be harmful and appropriate PPE must be used when using UV light. What is PPE? *(1 mark)*

....

Q4: Why is PPE used? *(1 mark)*

....

Q5: Give an example of PPE which would be appropriate for working with UV light. *(1 mark)*

....

A scientist performing a protein assay wanted to determine the concentration of protein in her sample. She performed a Bradford protein assay. Bradford reagent changes colour (and therefore absorbance) depending on the concentration of protein in the sample.

A buffer and Bradford reagent were added to the protein sample and the absorbance at 595nm was measured.

Q6: Why are buffers used in experiments such as this? *(1 mark)*

....

Q7: Name a piece of equipment that is used to measure the absorbance of a solution. *(1 mark)*

....

Q8: Use the following standard curve to estimate the protein concentration of a sample with an absorbance of 0.6.

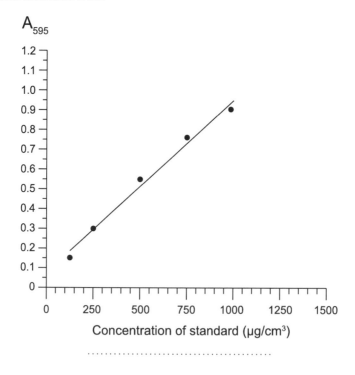

....

The following diagram shows some of the stages involved in producing a monoclonal antibody.

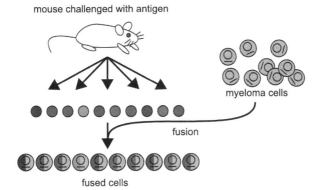

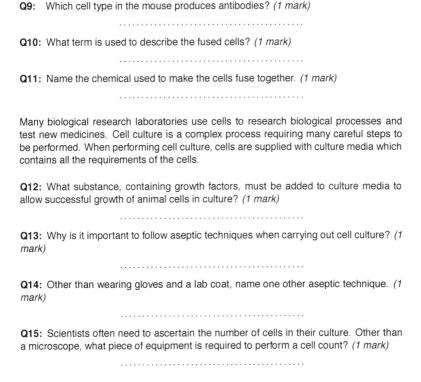

Q9: Which cell type in the mouse produces antibodies? *(1 mark)*

....

Q10: What term is used to describe the fused cells? *(1 mark)*

....

Q11: Name the chemical used to make the cells fuse together. *(1 mark)*

....

Many biological research laboratories use cells to research biological processes and test new medicines. Cell culture is a complex process requiring many careful steps to be performed. When performing cell culture, cells are supplied with culture media which contains all the requirements of the cells.

Q12: What substance, containing growth factors, must be added to culture media to allow successful growth of animal cells in culture? *(1 mark)*

....

Q13: Why is it important to follow aseptic techniques when carrying out cell culture? *(1 mark)*

....

Q14: Other than wearing gloves and a lab coat, name one other aseptic technique. *(1 mark)*

....

Q15: Scientists often need to ascertain the number of cells in their culture. Other than a microscope, what piece of equipment is required to perform a cell count? *(1 mark)*

....

....

Topic 2

Proteomics, protein structure, binding and conformational change

Contents

Prerequisite knowledge

You should already know that:

- *proteins are held in a three-dimensional shape;*

- *amino acids are linked by peptide bonds to form polypeptides;*

- *polypeptide chains fold to form the three-dimensional shape of a protein, which is held together by hydrogen bonds and other interactions between individual amino acids;*

- *the role of the active site in orientating reactants is lowering the activation energy of the transition state and the release of products with low affinity for the active site;*

- *there are three types of inhibition: competitive inhibition (binds to active site), non-competitive inhibition (changes shape of active site) and feedback inhibition (end product binds to an enzyme which catalyses a reaction earlier in the pathway).*

Learning objectives

By the end of this topic, you should be able to:

- *explain what the proteome is and why it is larger than the genome;*

- *state that DNA sequencing and microarray technology allow the routine analysis of the genome and transcriptome - however, the analysis of the proteome is far more complex;*

- *state that, as a result of gene expression, not all genes are expressed as proteins in a particular cell;*

- *state that the distinguishing feature of protein molecules is their folded nature, and their ability to bind tightly and specifically to other molecules;*

- *explain what a ligand is;*

- *describe the effects of a ligand binding to a protein;*

- *state that proteins may have one or more stable conformations depending on binding;*

- *describe the primary sequence of a protein;*

- *describe and identify forms of secondary structure, such as alpha helices, parallel or anti-parallel beta sheets, or turns;*

- *describe the role of hydrogen bonds in secondary protein structure;*

- *classify amino acids according to their R groups, including positively charged, negatively charged, polar, hydrophobic and other;*

- *describe the tertiary structure of a protein;*

- *describe the role of prosthetic groups in proteins, including the role of the haem prosthetic group in haemoglobin;*

- *describe the quaternary structure of a protein;*

- *explain that interactions of the R groups of amino acids can be influenced by temperature and pH;*

- *describe the fluid mosaic model of the plasma membrane;*

- *state that the R groups at the surface of a protein determine its location within a cell;*

- *describe the distribution of hydrophobic and hydrophilic R groups within a soluble protein found in the cytoplasm;*

- *describe the importance of hydrophobic R groups in allowing strong hydrophobic interactions that hold integral proteins within the phospholipid bilayer;*

- *state that some integral proteins are transmembrane, for example channels, transporters and many receptors;*

- state that peripheral proteins have fewer hydrophobic R groups interacting with the phospholipids;

- state that R groups not involved in protein folding can allow binding to ligands;

- describe the role of proteins which bind to DNA, including histones and those which stimulate or inhibit initiation of transcription;

- explain the consequences of ligand binding to the conformation of protein structure;

- describe the induced fit model of enzyme action;

- explain how the induced fit model reduces the activation energy for a reaction;

- describe the control of allosteric enzymes;

- describe the role of positive and negative modulators;

- state that some proteins with quaternary structure show cooperativity, in which changes in binding at one subunit alter the affinity of the remaining subunits'

- describe the role of cooperativity in the binding and release of oxygen in haemoglobin, and the influence of temperature and pH on this process;

- describe the effect of an addition or removal of a phosphate from a protein;

- describe the role of kinase and phosphatase enzymes;

- describe the role of ATPases;

- describe the role of myosin and actin proteins in muscle contraction.

2.1 Proteomics

The genome is all of the hereditary information encoded in DNA. The proteome is the entire set of proteins expressed by a genome. The proteome is larger than the genome due to alternative splicing and post-translational modification.

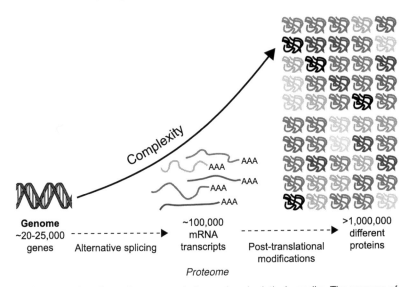

| Genome ~20-25,000 genes | Alternative splicing | ~100,000 mRNA transcripts | Post-translational modifications | >1,000,000 different proteins |

Proteome

DNA sequencing allows the genome to be analysed relatively easily. The process of DNA sequencing determines the order of the bases (A, T, G and C) in a strand of DNA. DNA sequencing can be performed on individual genes, chromosomes or entire genomes.

The collection of all RNA molecules produced by a genome is known as the transcriptome. These RNA molecules include messenger RNA (mRNA), transfer RNA (tRNA), ribosomal RNA (rRNA) and other non-coding RNA. Microarray analysis allows the transcriptome to be analysed. mRNA is extracted from a cell and an enzyme called reverse transcriptase is used to convert the mRNA into a DNA copy known as cDNA. The cDNA is labelled with a fluorescent probe. The cDNA is added to a microarray which contains known DNA sequences. A laser is used to identify if the cDNA has bound to any complementary DNA fragments on the microarray. This allows scientists to determine which genes are being expressed in different cell types.

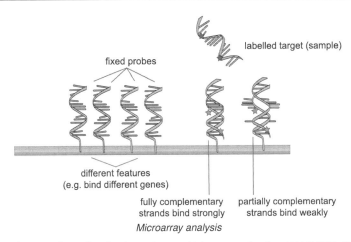

Microarray analysis

The microarray is analysed using a laser, which causes the fluorescent tags on the cDNA to fluoresce. The following image shows the results of microarray analysis.

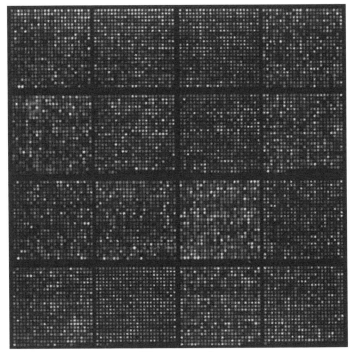

Microarray results

Proteomics refers to the study of proteins. Proteomics is much more complex than genomics or transcriptomics because the genome is relatively constant, whereas the proteins found in one cell type will differ from another cell type and may differ from time to time. Scientists are developing methods to analyse the proteome, but these are very complex and time consuming.

2.2   Protein structure

Proteins are vitally important molecules found within all living cells. The distinguishing feature of protein molecules is their folded nature, and their ability to bind tightly and specifically to other molecules. Proteins must be folded in a specific manner to allow them to function properly.

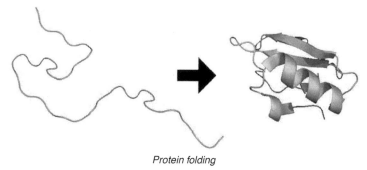

Protein folding

Many proteins bind to other molecules and their shapes must be complementary to allow this. Binding can cause a conformational change in the protein which may result in an altered function, and may be reversible. Proteins may have one or more stable conformations depending on binding.

Amino acids

Amino acids are the building blocks of proteins. They can be grouped according to their properties. All amino acids have a central carbon with four groups attached (an amine (NH_2), a carboxylic acid $(COOH)$, a hydrogen and a variable R group).

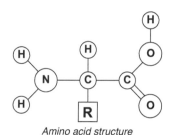

Amino acid structure

The R group attached to the central carbon determines the characteristics of that amino acid. Amino acids may be:

- negatively charged;

- positively charged;

- polar;

- hydrophobic;

- other.

Negatively charged amino acids are hydrophilic and the key component of their R group is a carboxylic acid group (negatively charged at pH 7). Positively charged amino acids are hydrophilic and the key component of their R group is an amine group (positively charged at pH 7). Polar amino acids are hydrophilic and the key component of their R group are hydrophilic groups, like carbonyl ($C=O$), hydroxyl (OH) or amine (NH) groups. Hydrophobic amino acids are non-polar and the key component of their R group is a hydrocarbon group.

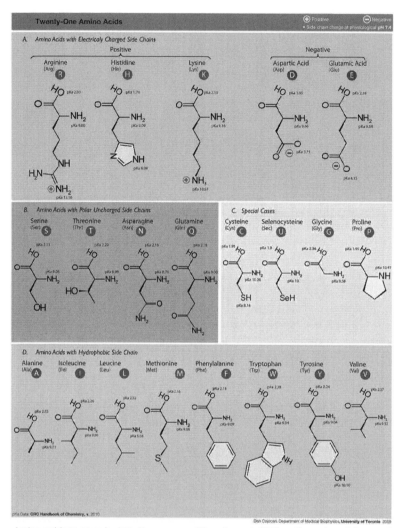

Amino acid structure by http://commons.wikimedia.org/wiki/User:Dancojocari, licenced
under the Creative Commons http://creativecommons.org/licenses/by-sa/3.0/deed.en
license

Primary sequence

Proteins are **polymers** of amino acid **monomers**. Amino acids link by peptide bonds to form polypeptides. The primary sequence is the order in which the amino acids are synthesised into the **polypeptide**.

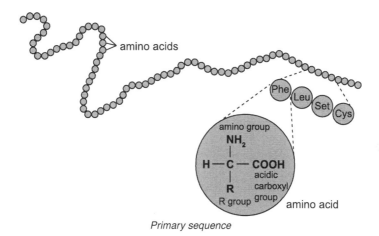

Primary sequence

Secondary sequence

The amino acids along the length of the polypeptide chain interact with one another. Some amino acids form hydrogen bonds which result in secondary protein structure.

The secondary structure of a protein is stabilised by hydrogen bonds between atoms of the same chain. α-helix is one type of secondary structure. It is a spiral with the R groups sticking outwards. Another type of secondary structure is β-sheet. β-sheet has parts of the chain running alongside each other, forming a sheet. The R groups sit above and below the sheet.

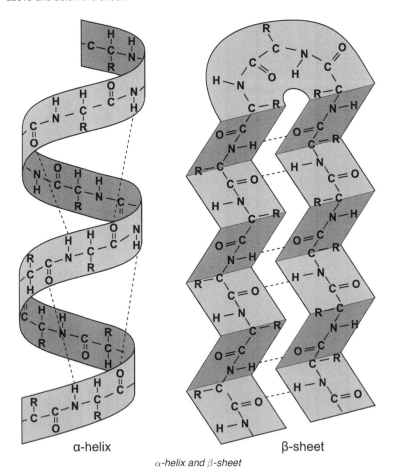

α-helix   β-sheet

α-helix and β-sheet

β-sheets are usually anti-parallel, meaning that the chains run in opposite directions from each other. They can also be parallel, meaning that the chains run in the same direction. The sheets are parallel or antiparallel depending on their N and C termini as shown in the following diagram.

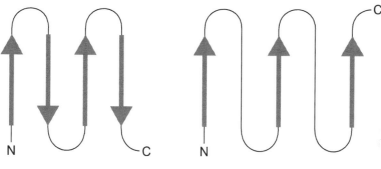

Antiparallel β-sheet   Parallel β-sheet

Antiparallel and parallel β-sheet

Turns are a third type of secondary structure; they reverse the direction of the polypeptide chain. The exact role of turns has not yet been determined, but some scientists believe that turns allow interactions between regular secondary structure elements.

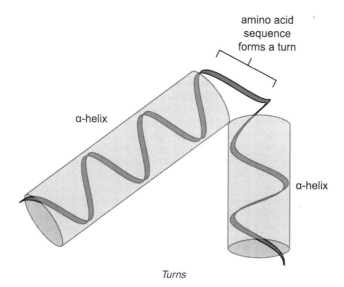

Turns

Tertiary structure

Tertiary structure refers to the overall folding of the polypeptide and its final shape. Folding at this level is stabilised by many different interactions between the R groups of the amino acids.

Tertiary structure is brought about by charge effects, such as interactions of the R groups in hydrophobic regions. Hydrophobic amino acids tend to cluster together on the interior of a protein, away from the surface. Hydrophilic amino acids will predominate at the surface of a soluble protein. This hydrophobic effect is one of the main driving forces of protein folding.

Ionic, hydrogen and disulfide bonds are also involved in tertiary structure. In an ionic bond, atoms are oppositely charged and, therefore, held by an electrostatic attraction. A hydrogen bond is an electromagnetic attractive interaction which occurs between a hydrogen atom and an electronegative atom, such as oxygen or nitrogen. A disulfide bond (also known as a disulfide bridge) is a covalent bond between two thiol (SH) groups.

One final charge effect which influences the tertiary structure of a protein is van der Waals interactions. Van der Waals interactions are caused by fluctuations in electron clouds around molecules which cause them to become slightly positively or negatively charged. These interactions may result in attraction or repulsion between atoms.

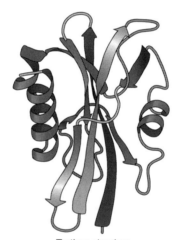

Tertiary structure

The tertiary structure of a protein may include prosthetic (non-protein) parts. **Prosthetic groups** give proteins added function, e.g. haem in haemoglobin. This haem group contains an iron atom which is the site of oxygen binding. The iron atom is covalently bound to the haemoglobin via a series of histidine amino acids.

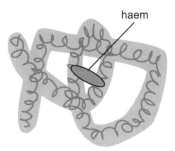

haem

Tertiary structure with prosthetic group

Quaternary structure

Many proteins are made up of more than one subunit. Quaternary structure exists in proteins with several connected polypeptide subunits which are linked by bonds between the R groups of the polypeptide chains. For example, haemoglobin is made of four subunits as shown in the following diagram.

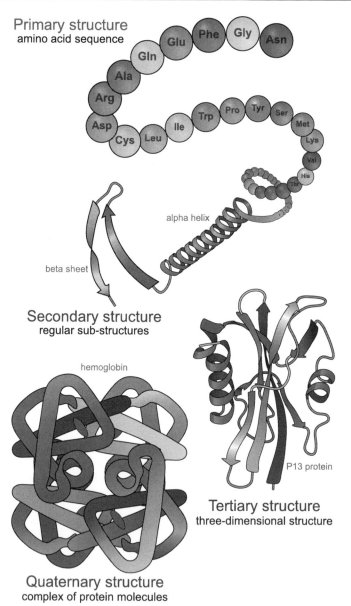

Primary structure
amino acid sequence

Secondary structure
regular sub-structures

alpha helix

beta sheet

hemoglobin

Quaternary structure
complex of protein molecules

P13 protein

Tertiary structure
three-dimensional structure

Protein structure

Interactions of the R groups can be influenced by pH and temperature. This is why pH
and temperature will affect the structure (and function) of a protein.

© HERIOT-WATT UNIVERSITY

2.3   Hydrophobic and hydrophilic interactions

The fluid mosaic model

The fluid mosaic model describes the structure of the plasma membrane.

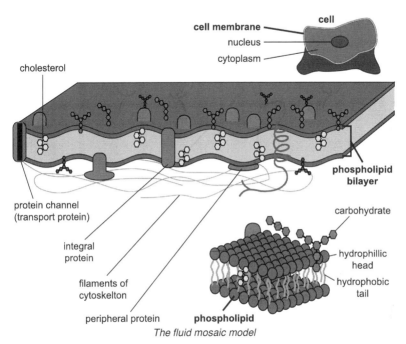

The fluid mosaic model

Membranes are comprised of a bilayer of phospholipid molecules and a patchwork of protein molecules. The head region of a phospholipid molecule is charged and, therefore, hydrophilic (attracted to water). The tail region is uncharged and non-polar, and, therefore, hydrophobic (repelled by water). The phospholipids are constantly changing position; this gives the membrane its fluid quality.

The cell membrane is embedded with proteins which form a patchy mosaic. Proteins found within the membrane can have many different functions. Membrane proteins can be classed as integral or peripheral.

Integral proteins are held firmly in place within the membrane. They are held in place by strong hydrophobic interactions with the lipid tails. Regions of hydrophobic R groups allow strong hydrophobic interactions that hold integral proteins within the phospholipid bilayer. Some integral proteins are transmembrane, this means that they span the entire width of the membrane. Examples of transmembrane protein include channels, transporters and many receptors.

Peripheral proteins are only loosely associated with the plasma membrane. Peripheral proteins have fewer hydrophobic R groups interacting with the phospholipids. They are held in place by charged or polar amino acids R groups or by hydrophobic interactions.

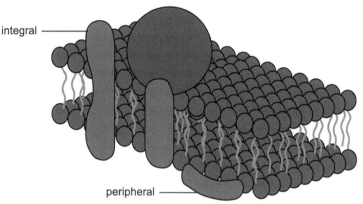

Peripheral and integral membrane proteins

Hydrophobic and hydrophilic interactions

The R groups at the surface of a protein determine its location within a cell. Hydrophilic R groups will predominate at the surface of a soluble protein found in the cytoplasm. In these proteins, hydrophobic R groups may cluster at the centre to form a globular structure.

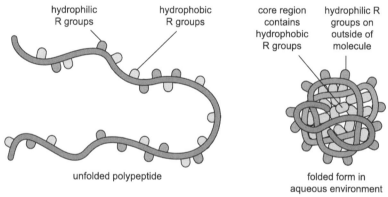

Protein folding

Hydrophobic and hydrophilic interactions also have implications for the folding of membrane proteins. Regions which span the membrane will have hydrophobic R groups towards the outside. Regions in contact with aqueous solutions will have hydrophilic R groups towards the outside.

2.4   Binding to ligands

A **ligand** is a substance that can bind to a protein.   R groups not involved in protein folding can allow binding to these other molecules.   Binding sites will have complementary shape and chemistry to the ligand.

DNA binds to a number of proteins. The sugar phosphate backbone of DNA is negatively charged, which allows it to bind to positively charged proteins. DNA-protein interactions are especially important in the packaging of DNA into chromosomes to allow DNA to fit inside the nucleus of a cell. Positively charged histone proteins bind to the negatively charged sugar-phosphate backbone of DNA in eukaryotes. The DNA is wrapped around histones to form nucleosomes, packing the DNA in chromosomes.

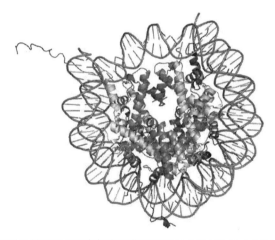

DNA bound to histone protein by http://commons.wikimedia.org/wiki/User:Emw,
licenced under the Creative Commons http://creativecommons.org/licenses/by-sa/3.0/d
eed.en license

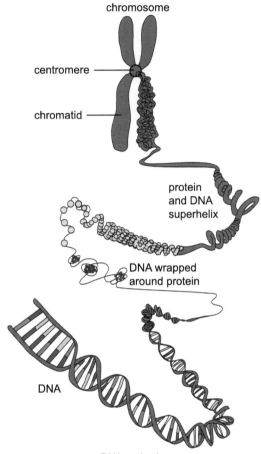

DNA packaging

Other proteins have binding sites that are specific to particular sequences of double stranded DNA and, when bound, can either stimulate or inhibit the initiation of transcription. For example, activator proteins bind to specific DNA sequences and stimulate transcription of downstream genes. Activator proteins bind to regions of DNA known as enhancers, and help to recruit transcription factors and RNA polymerase to the promoter region of the gene to be transcribed.

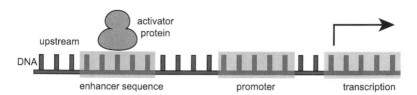

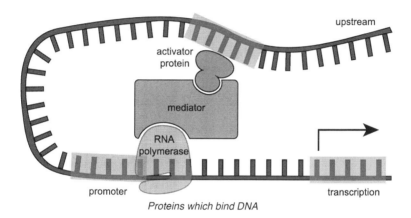

Proteins which bind DNA

2.5   Ligand binding changes the conformation of a protein

Induced fit

The energy needed to allow a reaction to occur is called the activation energy. If a catalyst is absent, the activation energy is quite large and the speed of the reaction extremely slow. The presence of a catalyst ensures that the activation energy is lowered and that the reaction takes place faster. In living systems, an enzyme lowers the activation energy by forming an enzyme-substrate complex that accelerates the rate of reaction. It is like rolling a boulder down a hill, but having to push it up a small hump first - this initial push takes energy, but after that the boulder rolls on. Enzymes make the small hump even smaller!

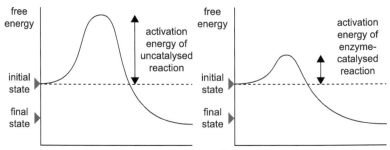

Effect of an enzyme on activation energy

As a **ligand** binds to a protein binding site or a substrate binds to an enzyme's **active site**, the conformation of the protein changes. This change in conformation causes a functional change in the protein. In enzymes, specificity between the active site and substrate is related to induced fit.

The induced fit model of enzyme action states that, when the correct substrate starts to bind to the enzyme, there is a temporary change in the shape of the enzyme active site. This change in shape increases the binding and interaction of the substrate with the enzyme. The chemical environment that is produced lowers the activation energy which is required for the reaction. Once the reaction has taken place, the original enzyme conformation is resumed and products are released from the active site.

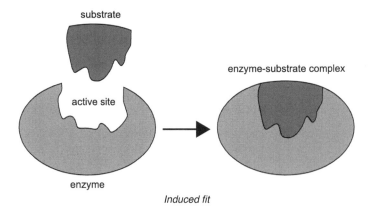

Induced fit

Allosteric enzymes

An allosteric enzyme is one which changes conformation upon binding a modulator. In allosteric enzymes, modulators bind at secondary binding sites, known as allosteric sites. These allosteric sites are separate and distinct from the active site of the enzyme. Upon binding a modulator, the conformation of an allosteric enzyme will change and this alters the affinity of the active site for the substrate. Modulators may be positive or negative. Negative modulators reduce the enzyme's affinity for the substrate and positive modulators increase the enzyme's affinity for the substrate.

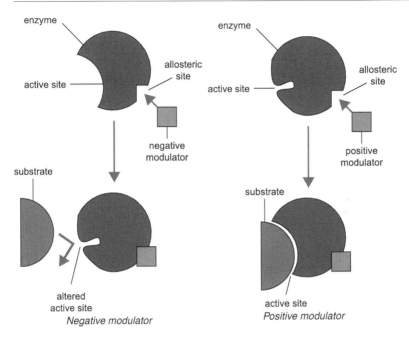

Negative modulator

Positive modulator

Cooperativity

Some proteins with quaternary structure show cooperativity in which changes in binding at one subunit alter the affinity of the remaining subunits.

Haemoglobin shows cooperativity. Haemoglobin demonstrates quaternary structure in that is made up of four **polypeptide** subunits, each of which contain a haem group capable of binding a molecule of oxygen. When one of the subunits binds a molecule of oxygen, the second binds more easily, and the third and fourth easier still. This process is known as cooperativity; the ligand binding to one subunit of the protein has increased the other subunits' affinity for the ligand. When oxy-haemoglobin releases oxygen the same process happens; once one subunit has released its oxygen, the next subunit is more likely to release its oxygen and so on.

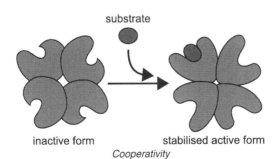

Cooperativity

The main factors which effect haemoglobin's ability to bind oxygen are:

- temperature - as temperature increases, affinity for oxygen decreases;

- pH - as pH decreases, affinity for oxygen decreases.

The following graph shows the partial pressure of oxygen in the blood versus oxyhaemglobin saturation (known as the oxygen-haemoglobin dissociation curve). The blue line represents standard physiological conditions, the red line represents the effect of decreasing pH or increasing temperature, and the green line represents the effect of increasing pH or decreasing temperature.

At a partial oxygen pressure (PO_2) of 50 mmHg in normal physiological conditions, approximately 80% of haemoglobin is saturated; a decrease in pH or an increase in temperature reduces this value to nearer 75%. This change in saturation is caused by a decrease in haemoglobin's affinity for oxygen.

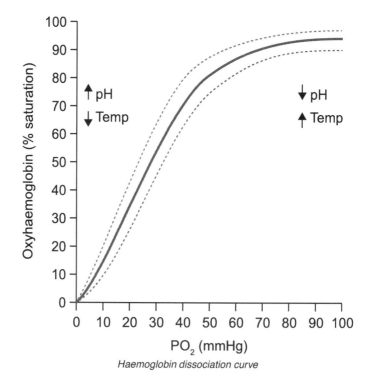

Haemoglobin dissociation curve

2.6   Reversible binding of phosphate and control of conformation

Phosphorylation

Phosphorylation of proteins is a form of post-translational modification.   The addition or removal of phosphate from particular R groups can be used to cause reversible conformational changes in proteins.   Phosphorylation/dephosphorylation allows the activity of many cellular proteins, such as enzymes and receptors, to be regulated. Kinase enzymes are often responsible for phosphorylation of other proteins. Phosphatase enzymes catalyse dephosphorylation.

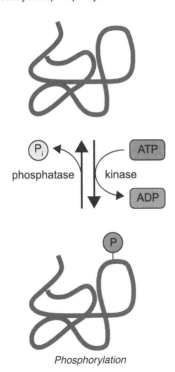

Phosphorylation

Actin and myosin - muscle contraction

A sarcomere is the basic unit of a muscle. Sarcomeres contain fibrous proteins called actin and myosin. The action of actin and myosin sliding past each other allows muscles to contract and relax. Myosin has heads that act as cross bridges as they bind to actin. When ATP binds to myosin, the myosin head detaches from actin, swings forwards and rebinds. The rebinding releases the ADP and a phosphate; this drags the myosin along the actin filament. This sliding motion shortens the sarcomere and brings about muscle contraction.

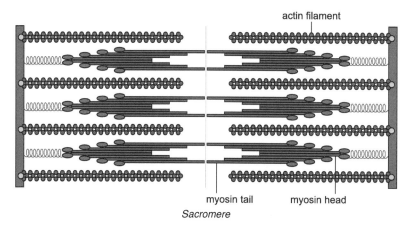

Sacromere

Muscle contraction involves the following stages.

1. Muscle contraction occurs when the muscle receives an impulse from a nerve cell.

2. The impulse causes myosin binding sites on actin to be exposed.

3. The myosin heads form a flexed shape and bind to the actin.

4. ADP and P_i are released from the myosin, causing it to return to its relaxed shape; this moves the actin filament to the centre of the sarcomere.

5. ATP binds to the myosin head, which causes it to release the actin.

6. The myosin head acts as an ATPase; it breaks down the ATP to ADP + P_i, causing the head of the myosin to flex again.

© HERIOT-WATT UNIVERSITY

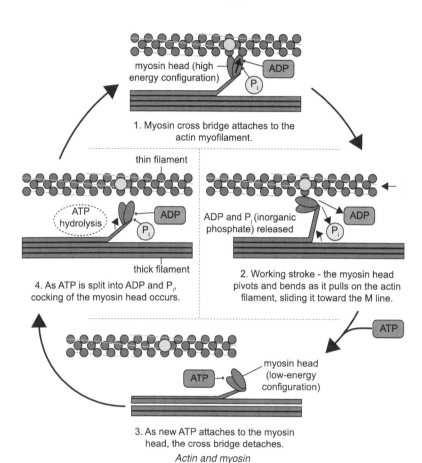

Actin and myosin

2.7   Learning points

Summary

- The proteome is the entire set of proteins expressed by a genome. The proteome is larger than the genome due to alternative splicing and post-translational modification.

- DNA sequencing and microarray technology allow the routine analysis of the genome and transcriptome, however, the analysis of the proteome is far more complex.

- As a result of gene expression, not all genes are expressed as proteins in a particular cell.

- The distinguishing feature of protein molecules is their folded nature, and their ability to bind tightly and specifically to other molecules.

- A ligand is a substance that can bind to a protein.

- As a ligand binds to a protein binding site or a substrate binds to an enzyme's active site, the conformation of the protein changes. This change in conformation causes a functional change in the protein.

- Proteins may have one or more stable conformations depending on binding.

- The primary sequence is the order in which the amino acids are synthesised into the polypeptide.

- Hydrogen bonding along the backbone of the protein strand results in regions of secondary structure - alpha helices, parallel or antiparallel beta sheets, or turns.

- Amino acids may be positively charged, negatively charged, polar, hydrophobic or 'other' according to their R groups.

- The polypeptide folds into a tertiary structure; the final 3D shape of the polypeptide.

- Prosthetic groups give proteins added function, e.g. haem in haemoglobin.

- Quaternary structure exists in proteins with several connected polypeptide subunits.

- Interactions of the R groups of amino acids can be influenced by temperature and pH.

- The fluid mosaic model describes the structure of the plasma membrane. Membranes are comprised of a bilayer of phospholipid molecules and a patchwork of protein molecules.

- The R groups at the surface of a protein determine its location within a cell.

Summary continued

- Hydrophilic R groups will predominate at the surface of a soluble protein found in the cytoplasm. In these proteins, hydrophobic R groups may cluster at the centre to form a globular structure.

- Regions of hydrophobic R groups allow strong hydrophobic interactions that hold integral proteins within the phospholipid bilayer.

- Some integral proteins are transmembrane, for example channels, transporters and many receptors.

- Peripheral proteins have fewer hydrophobic R groups interacting with the phospholipids.

- R groups not involved in protein folding can allow binding to ligands.

- DNA binds to a number of proteins. Positively charged histone proteins bind to the negatively charged sugar-phosphate backbone of DNA in eukaryotes; the DNA is wrapped around histones to form nucleosomes, allowing efficient packing of the DNA into chromosomes.

- Other proteins have binding sites that are specific to particular sequences of double-stranded DNA and, when bound, can either stimulate or inhibit initiation of transcription.

- As a ligand binds to a protein binding site or a substrate binds to an enzyme's active site, the conformation of the protein changes.

- When the correct substrate starts to bind, a temporary change in shape of the active site occurs, increasing the binding and interaction with the substrate. The chemical environment produced lowers the activation energy required for the reaction. Once catalysis takes place, the original enzyme conformation is resumed and products are released from the active site.

- In allosteric enzymes, modulators bind at secondary binding sites. The conformation of the enzyme changes and this alters the affinity of the active site for the substrate.

- Positive modulators increase the enzyme's affinity whereas negative modulators reduce the enzyme's affinity for the substrate.

- Some proteins with quaternary structure show cooperativity in which changes in binding at one subunit alter the affinity of the remaining subunits.

- In haemoglobin, when one of the subunits binds a molecule of oxygen, the second binds more easily, and the third and fourth easier still. This process is known as cooperativity.

- When oxy-haemoglobin releases oxygen, the same process as above happens; once one subunit has released its oxygen the next subunit is more likely to release its oxygen and so on.

- The main factors which will affect haemoglobin's ability to bind oxygen are:

Summary continued

- ○ temperature - as temperature increases, affinity for oxygen decreases;
- ○ pH - as pH decreases, affinity for oxygen decreases.

- The addition or removal of phosphate from particular R groups can be used to cause reversible conformational changes in proteins. This is a common form of post-translational modification.

- Kinase is often responsible for phosphorylation of other proteins and phosphatase catalyses dephosphorylation.

- ATPases use ATP for their phosphorylation.

- In muscle contraction, myosin has heads that act as cross bridges as they bind to actin. When ATP binds to myosin, the myosin head detaches from actin, swings forwards and rebinds. The rebinding releases the ADP and a phosphate and drags the myosin along the actin filament.

2.8   Extended response questions

The activities which follow present extended response questions similar to the style that you will encounter in the examination.

You should have a good understanding of the structure of proteins and enzyme activity before attempting the questions.

You should give your completed answers to your teacher or tutor for marking, or try to mark them yourself using the suggested marking schemes.

Extended response question: Structure of proteins

Give details of the structure of proteins including primary, secondary, tertiary and quaternary levels. *(10 marks)*

. . . .

Extended response question: Enzyme activity

Give an account of enzyme activity under the following headings:

- induced fit; *(4 marks)*
- enzyme activation. *(5 marks)*

. . . .

2.9   End of topic test

End of Topic 2 test

Q1:   What is a proteome? *(1 mark)*

Go online

....

Q2:   What is the primary protein sequence? *(1 mark)*

....

The following illustration shows the structure of insulin.

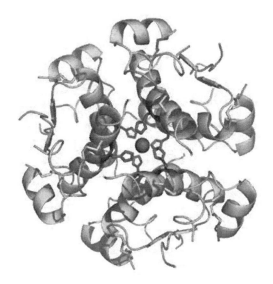

Insulin hexamer by Isaac Yonemoto, licenced under the Creative Commons http://creati
vecommons.org/licenses/by/2.5/deed.en license

Q3:   What aspect(s) of the secondary structure of proteins can be seen in the
illustration? *(1 mark)*

....

Q4:   What aspect(s) of the tertiary structure of proteins can be seen in the illustration?
(1 mark)

....

Q5:   What aspect(s) of the quaternary structure of proteins can be seen in the
illustration? *(1 mark)*

....

Q6: The R groups at the surface of a protein determine its location within a cell.
_____ R groups will predominate at the surface of a soluble protein found in the
cytoplasm. *(1 mark)*

....

Q7: In the soluble protein found in the cytoplasm, _____ R groups may cluster at
the centre to form a globular structure. *(1 mark)*

....

The following diagram shows a series of proteins in a section of plasma membrane.

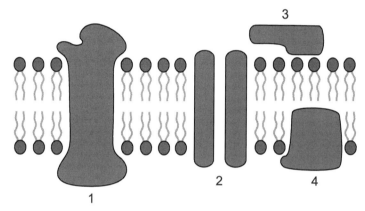

Q8: Which number(s) in the diagram represent integral protein? *(1 mark)*

....

Q9: Which number(s) in the diagram represent peripheral protein? *(1 mark)*

....

Q10: How are integral proteins held within the membrane? *(1 mark)*

....

Q11: What is the function of the protein labelled number 2 in the diagram? *(1 mark)*

....

Q12: What is a ligand?

....

The following diagram shows DNA wrapped around histone protein.

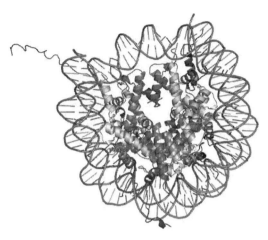

DNA bound to histone protein by http://commons.wikimedia.org/wiki/User:Emw,
licenced under the Creative Commons http://creativecommons.org/licenses/by-sa/3.0/d
eed.en license

Q13: What aspect of secondary structure can be seen in the histone protein? *(1 mark)*

....

Q14: Explain how DNA is able to bind to histone proteins. *(1 mark)*

....

Q15: What type of enzyme is responsible for phosphorylation of other proteins? *(1 mark)*

....

Q16: What type of enzyme catalyses dephosphorylation? *(1 mark)*

....

Q17: What name is given to proteins which use ATP for their phosphorylation? *(1 mark)*

....

....

Topic 3

Membrane proteins

Contents

Prerequisite knowledge

You should already know that:

- *cells are specialised to perform specific functions;*

- *passive processes do not require energy;*

- *active processes require energy.*

Learning objectives

By the end of this topic, you should be able to:

- *state that the phospholipid bilayer acts as a barrier to ions and most uncharged polar molecules;*

- *describe the role of transmembrane proteins, including channel and transporter proteins;*

- *state that, to perform specialised functions, different cell types and different cell compartments have different channel and transporter proteins;*

- *state that the passage of molecules through channel proteins is passive (e.g. aquaporin);*

- *explain what is meant by the term ligand-gated and voltage-gated channels;*

- *state that transporter proteins change conformation to transport molecules across a membrane;*

- *state that transport can be facilitated (e.g. glucose symport) or active (e.g. Na/K-ATPase);*

- *explain what is meant by the term signal transduction;*

- *describe the consequences of signal transduction with reference to activation of enzymes or G-proteins, a change in uptake or secretion of molecules, rearrangement of the cytoskeleton or activation of proteins that regulate gene transcription;*

- *describe the action and functions of the sodium-potassium pump (Na/K-ATPase);*

- *state that the maintenance of ion gradients by Na/K-ATPase accounts for a significant part of basal metabolic rate (up to 25% in humans);*

- *state that nerve transmission is a wave of depolarisation of the resting potential of a neuron;*

- *describe how a nerve impulse is brought about;*

- *describe the roles of ligand-gated and voltage-gated ion channels in the transmission of nerve impulses;*

- *explain what is meant by the term resting membrane potential.*

3.1 Movement of molecules across membranes

The phospholipid bilayer acts as a barrier to ions and most uncharged polar molecules due to its hydrophobic nature. Many molecules, therefore, must pass across the membrane with the help of proteins. These transmembrane proteins (which act as channels or transporters) control the concentration of ions and other molecules within the cell. To perform specialised functions, different cell types and different cell compartments have different channel and transporter proteins.

Channel proteins allow molecules to move from one side of the membrane to the other without using energy (**passive** transport). Water can pass across the plasma membrane by diffusing through the phospholipid bilayer or through water channels which are called aquaporins. Water diffuses very slowly across the plasma membrane; most water passes across the membrane via aquaporin which can allow up to 3 billion water molecules to move across the membrane per second. The direction of water movement is dependent upon the osmotic gradient.

aquaporin

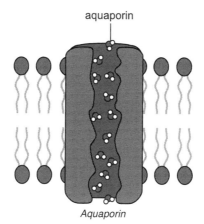

Aquaporin

Some channel proteins are gated and change **conformation** to allow or prevent diffusion. Gated channels respond to a stimulus which causes them to open or close. The stimulus may be chemical (ligand-gated) or electrical (voltage-gated).

Ligand-gated channels are controlled by signal molecules.

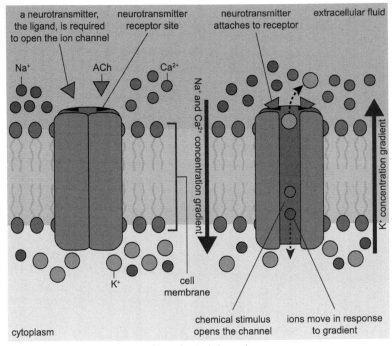

Ligand-gated channel

Voltage-gated channels are controlled by changes in ion concentrations.

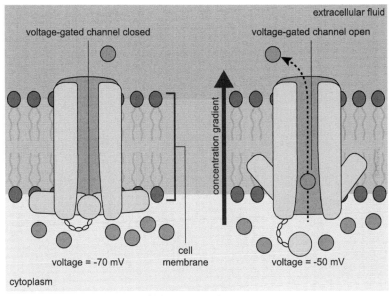

Voltage-gated channel

Transporter proteins change conformation to transport molecules across a membrane. They work by one of two mechanisms:

- facilitated;
- **active**.

Facilitated transport is a passive process, meaning that it does not require energy. It differs from passive transport through channel proteins in that facilitated transport involves a conformational change in the protein. Glucose moves across the membrane by facilitated transport.

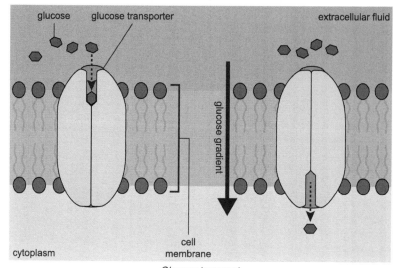

Glucose transport

Some transporter proteins require energy to bring about the necessary conformational change. In this case, the transport is active (requires energy). The conformational change in active transport requires energy from hydrolysis of ATP. One example is the sodium-potassium pump (Na/K-ATPase).

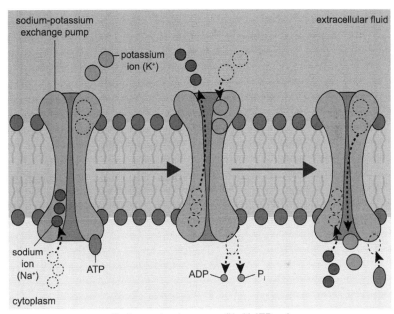

Sodium-potassium pump (Na/K-ATPase)

3.2   Signal transduction

Some proteins in the plasma membrane act as receptors. Receptor proteins convert an **extracellular** chemical signal to a specific **intracellular** response through a signal transduction pathway.

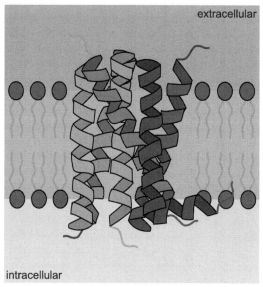

Protein receptor

The following activity shows how a signal transduction pathway links an extracellular chemical stimulus to a specific cellular response.

Signal transduction pathway

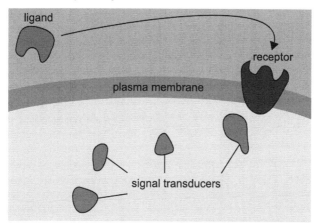

Go online

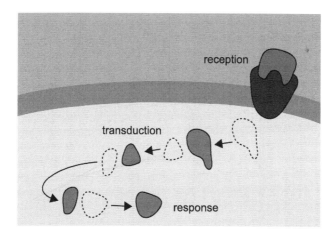

. . . .

Signal transduction may result in the activation of an enzyme or **G-protein**. An activated enzyme will bring about a specific chemical reaction within the cell. G-proteins are involved in transmitting signals from outside the cell into the cell. G-proteins can be 'switched on' or activated by binding GTP; they can also be 'switched off' or deactivated by binding GDP.

G-protein linked receptors

Go online

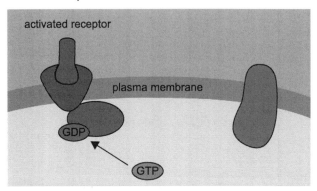

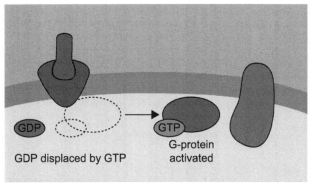

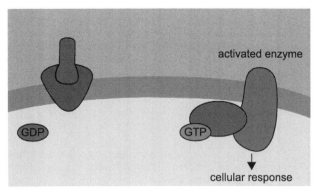

. . . .

Signal transduction may result in a change in the uptake or secretion of a molecule. For example, upon binding insulin, a cell will increase its glucose uptake. Signal transduction may also result in rearrangement of the cytoskeleton, a network of protein fibres which spans the length and breadth of a cell. It is found attached to membrane proteins and provides mechanical support for the cell. Processes such as movement require rearrangement of the cytoskeleton. Finally, signal transduction may also result in the activation of proteins that regulate gene transcription as shown in the following diagram.

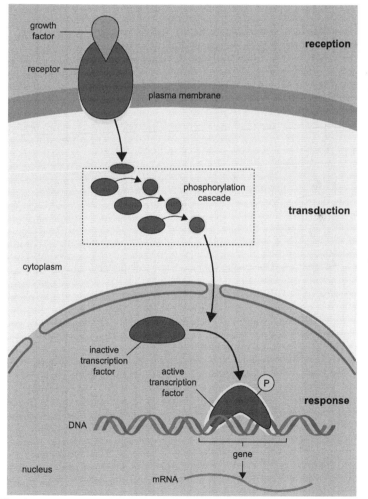

Signal transduction resulting in activation of proteins that regulate gene transcription

3.3   Ion transport pumps

The sodium-potassium pump (also known as Na/K-ATPase) transports ions against a steep concentration gradient using energy directly from ATP. It transports sodium ions out of cells and potassium ions in. The maintenance of ion gradients by Na/K-ATPase accounts for a significant part of basal metabolic rate (up to 25% in humans).

a) The transporter protein has high affinity for sodium ions inside the cell therefore binding occurs.

b) Phosphorylation by ATP causes the **conformation** of the protein to change.

c) The affinity for ions changes resulting in sodium being released outside of the cell.

d) Potassium ions from outside the cell bind to the sodium-potassium pump.

e) Dephosphorylation occurs which causes the conformation of the protein to change.

f)   Potassium ions are taken into the cell and the affinity returns to the start.

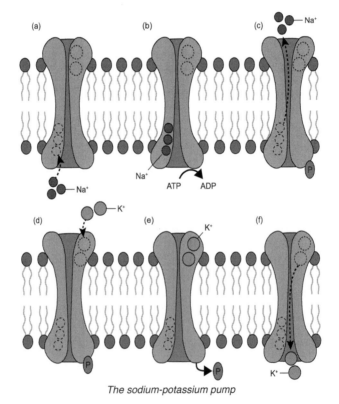

The sodium-potassium pump

Functions of the sodium-potassium pump include the following:

- maintaining the osmotic balance in animal cells;
- generation of the ion gradient for glucose **symport** in small intestine;
- generation and long-term maintenance of ion gradient for resting potential in neurons;
- generation of ion gradient in kidney tubules.

Sodium-potassium pump

Q1: Put the following steps that describe the actions of the sodium-potassium pump into the correct order.

Go online

- Dephosphorylation occurs, which causes the conformation of the protein to change.
- Potassium ions are taken into the cell and the affinity returns to the start.
- Phosphorylation by ATP causes the conformation of the protein to change.
- Potassium ions from outside the cell bind to the sodium-potassium pump.
- The transporter protein has high affinity for sodium ions inside the cell, therefore binding occurs.
- The affinity for ions changes, resulting in sodium being released outside of the cell.

. . . .

3.4   Ion channels and nerve transmission

All cells have an electrical potential difference (voltage) across their plasma membrane. This voltage is called the membrane potential. In neurons, the membrane potential is typically between -60 and -80mV (millivolts) when the cell is not transmitting signals. The minus sign means that the inside of the cell is negative relative to the outside.

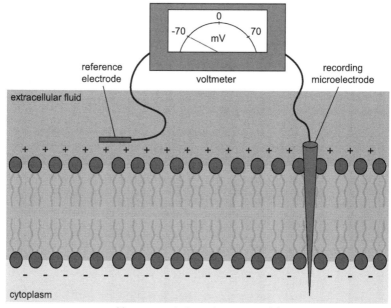

Measurement of membrane potential

The membrane potential of a neuron that is not transmitting signals is called the resting potential. The resting potential is generated and maintained by the action of the sodium-potassium pump, removing three positively charged sodium ions from the cell and only allowing two positively charged potassium ions into the cell.

Nerve transmission is a wave of **depolarisation** of the resting potential of a neuron. This can be stimulated when an appropriate signal molecule, such as a neurotransmitter, triggers the opening of ligand-gated ion channels. When a ligand-gated ion channel opens in response to a neurotransmitter, it may trigger depolarisation. This means the resting potential of the membrane increases. If the change is big enough it may trigger an action potential (a signal that carries information along axons).

Nerve transmission involves the following changes:

- when not sending signals, the resting potential across the plasma membrane is around -70mV;

- a neurotransmitter acts as a ligand and opens ligand-gated ion channels in the neuron membrane;

- this allows ions to enter the neuron and the voltage (membrane potential) changes;

- the change in voltage triggers opening of voltage-gated channels;

- a sequence of voltage-gated channels open resulting in a wave of depolarisation;

- once the wave of depolarisation has passed, these channel proteins close and others open to allow the movement of ions in the opposite direction to restore the resting potential.

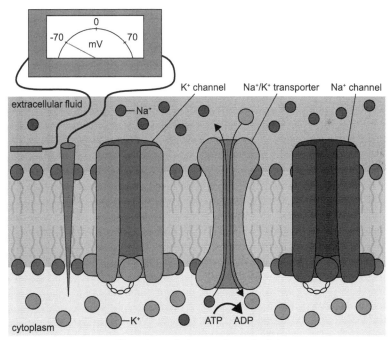

Nerve transmission - resting potential

At the resting potential, all voltage-gated Na$^+$ channels and most voltage-gated K$^+$ channels are closed. The Na$^+$/K$^+$ transporter pumps K$^+$ ions into the cell and Na$^+$ ions out.

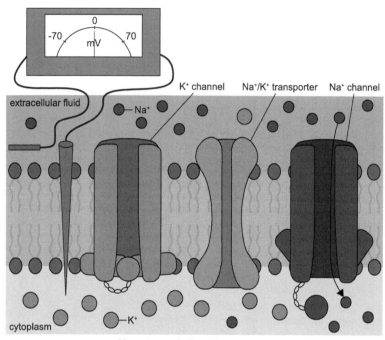

Nerve transmission - depolarisation

In response to a depolarisation, some Na+ channels open, allowing Na+ ions to enter the cell. The membrane starts to depolarise (the charge across the membrane lessens). If the threshold of excitation is reached, all of the Na+channels open.

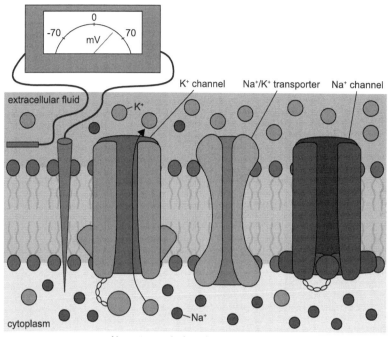

Nerve transmission - hyperpolarisation

At the peak action potential, Na⁺ channels close while K⁺ channels open. K⁺ leaves the cell and the membrane eventually becomes hyperpolarised.

The following graph shows the change in membrane potential as an impulse is passed along a neuron.

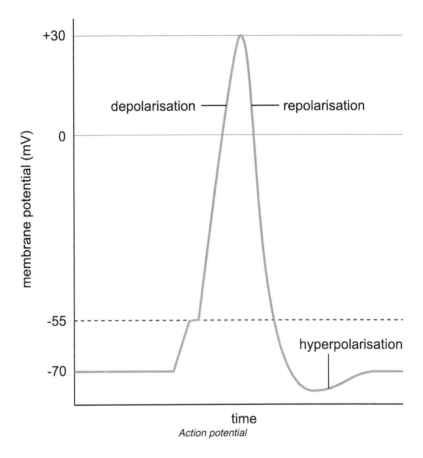

Action potential

3.5   Learning points

Summary

* The phospholipid bilayer acts as a barrier to ions and most uncharged polar molecules.

* To perform specialised functions, different cell types and cell compartments have different channel and transporter proteins.

* The passage of molecules through channel proteins is passive (e.g. aquaporin).

* Gated channels are controlled by signal molecules (ligand-gated channels) or changes in ion concentrations (voltage-gated channels).

* Transporter proteins change conformation to transport molecules across a membrane.

* Transport can be facilitated (e.g. glucose symport) or active (e.g. Na/K-ATPase).

* Signal transduction connects extracellular chemical signals to intracellular responses.

* Signal transduction may result in activation of enzymes or G-proteins, a change in uptake or secretion of molecules, rearrangement of the cytoskeleton or activation of proteins that regulate gene transcription.

* The sodium-potassium pump has high affinity for sodium ions inside the cell, therefore binding occurs. Phosphorylation by ATP causes the conformation of the protein to change. The affinity for ions changes, resulting in sodium being released outside of the cell. Potassium ions from outside the cell bind to the sodium-potassium pump. Dephosphorylation occurs, which causes the conformation of the protein to change. Potassium ions are taken into the cell and the affinity returns to the start.

* Functions of the sodium-potassium pump include the following:

  ○ maintaining the osmotic balance in animal cells;

  ○ generation of the ion gradient for glucose symport in the small intestine;

  ○ generation and long-term maintenance of the ion gradient for resting potential in neurons;

  ○ generation of the ion gradient in kidney tubules.

* The maintenance of ion gradients by Na/K-ATPase accounts for a significant part of basal metabolic rate (up to 25% in humans).

* Nerve transmission is a wave of depolarisation of the resting potential of a neuron.

Summary continued

- All cells have an electrical potential difference (voltage) across their plasma membrane. The membrane potential of a neuron that is not transmitting signals is called the resting potential.

- Nerve transmission can be stimulated when an appropriate signal molecule, such as a neurotransmitter, triggers the opening of ligand-gated ion channels. If sufficient ion movement occurs, then voltage-gated ion channels will open and the effect travels along the length of the nerve. Once the wave of depolarisation has passed, these channel proteins close and others open to allow the movement of ions in the opposite direction to restore the resting potential.

3.6   Extended response question

The activity which follows presents an extended response question similar to the style that you will encounter in the examination.

You should have a good understanding of the movement of ions across membranes before attempting the question.

You should give your completed answer to your teacher or tutor for marking, or try to mark it yourself using the suggested marking scheme.

Extended response question: Movement of ions across membranes

Discuss the movement of ions across membranes under the following headings:

- mechanism and functions of Na/K-ATPase; *(6 marks)*
- nerve transmission. *(4 marks)*

. . . .

3.7 End of topic test

End of Topic 3 test

Go online

Q2: Facilitated transport through transporter proteins is a _____ process, meaning that it does not require energy. *(1 mark)*

....

Q3: Some transporter proteins require energy to bring about the necessary conformational change. In this case the transport is _____. *(1 mark)*

....

Q4: What type of channel is shown in the following diagram? *(1 mark)*

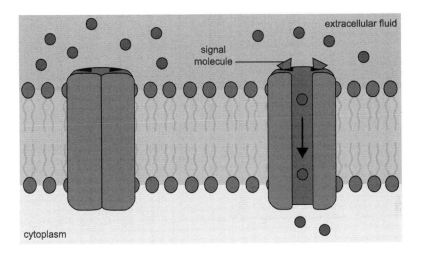

....

Q5: What term describes the action of membrane receptors in which signal binding triggers an event in the cytoplasm that alters the behaviour of the cell? *(1 mark)*

....

The following diagram shows the sodium-potassium pump.

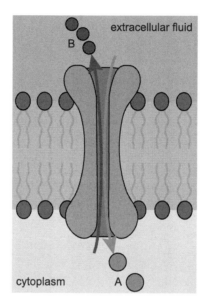

Q6: Which ions are represented by the letter A in the diagram? *(1 mark)*

a) Potassium
b) Sodium

. . . .

Q7: Which ions are represented by the letter B in the diagram? *(1 mark)*

a) Potassium
b) Sodium

. . . .

Q8: The sodium-potassium pump requires energy supplied by _____. *(1 mark)*

. . . .

Q9: Explain what happens when the sodium-potassium pump becomes phosphorylated. *(2 marks)*

. . . .

Q10: The sodium-potassium pump moves ions on the ratio 3 sodium : 2 potassium. If 10,000 of these ions are pumped across the membrane every 10 seconds, how many sodium ions are moved across in one minute? *(1 mark)*

. . . .

Q11: What name is given to the electrical potential difference (voltage) across the plasma membrane of a cell? *(1 mark)*

....

Q12: Nerve transmission can be stimulated when an appropriate signal molecule triggers the opening of ligand-gated ion channels.
What type of signalling molecule can stimulate nerve transmission? *(1 mark)*

....

Q13: Ligand-gated ion channels allow ions to enter the cells and change the electrical potential difference across the membrane.
What type of membrane channel will open in response to a change in ion concentrations? *(1 mark)*

....

Q14: Nerve transmission is a wave of _____ of the resting potential of a neuron. *(1 mark)*

....

....

© HERIOT-WATT UNIVERSITY

Topic 4

Detecting and amplifying an environmental stimulus

Contents

Prerequisite knowledge

You should already know that:

- *the three domains of life are bacteria, archaea and eukaryotes;*

- *ATP synthase is the enzyme that is required to synthesise ATP.*

Learning objectives

By the end of this topic, you should be able to:

- *state that photoreceptor protein systems are found across the three domains;*

- *explain how bacteriorhodopsin brings about the production of ATP;*

- *explain how photosynthetic pigments in plants allow generation of ATP;*

- *state that, in animals, the light-sensitive molecule retinal is combined with a membrane protein called opsin, forming rhodopsin;*

- *describe the role of cone cells in the process of sensing light by animals;*

- *describe the role of rod cells in the process of sensing light by animals;*

- *state that, when stimulated by one photon, a rhodopsin molecule activates hundreds of G-protein molecules which activate hundreds of molecules of an enzyme; if the enzyme triggers sufficient product formation, a nerve impulse may be generated.*

4.1   Photoreceptor protein systems in archaea

Some proteins are light sensitive, which means that they are capable of sensing and responding to light. These proteins are known as photoreceptor proteins. Photoreceptor protein systems are found across the three domains of life (prokaryotes, eukaryotes and **archaea**).   Bacteriorhodopsin is a photoreceptor protein used by archaea. Bacteriorhodopsin molecules generate potential differences by absorbing light to pump **protons** across the membrane. The protons return through **ATP synthase**, generating ATP, thus allowing archaea to convert light energy into chemical energy in the form of ATP.

Bacteriorhodopsin is a membrane protein which contains three polypeptide chains.   A light-absorbing molecule called **retinal** can be found inside each polypeptide chain of the protein. The following diagram shows one of the bacteriorhodopsin polypeptide chains with the retinal molecule shown in purple in the middle.

Bacteriorhodopsin

When a photon of light is absorbed, it causes a change in the **conformation** (shape) of the retinal molecule.   The retinal changes from a straight form to a bent form; it is this change in shape that allows protons to be pumped across the membrane by bacteriorhodopsin. The protons which are pumped across the membrane return through ATP synthase, resulting in the production of ATP. This process is shown in the following diagram.

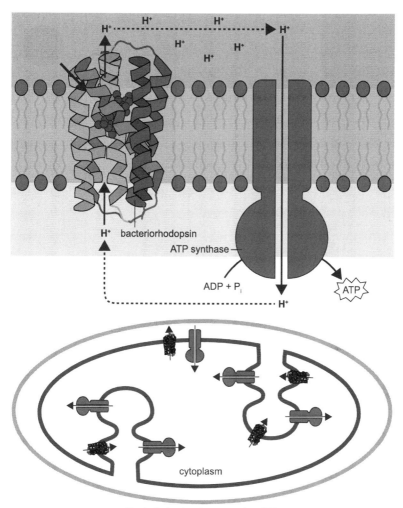

Bacteriorhodopsin generating ATP

4.2 Photoreceptor protein systems in plants

Plants use the photosynthetic pigment chlorophyll to convert light energy into chemical energy. Plant photosynthetic pigments are found within the chloroplasts. More specifically, they are found within membrane-bound compartments called grana. The membrane surrounding this structure is called the **thylakoid** membrane.

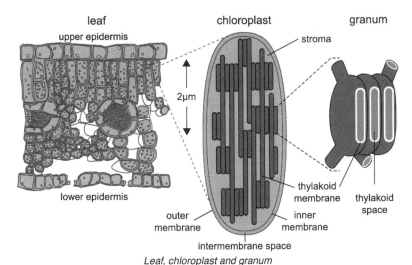

Leaf, chloroplast and granum

In plants, chlorophyll (and other photosynthetic pigments) is found bound to protein molecules to form protein photosystems. When a molecule of chlorophyll absorbs light, one of its electrons is boosted to a higher energy level. The electron then passes along a series of protein carriers (an electron transport chain). As the electron moves along the series of proteins, hydrogen ions are pumped across the thylakoid membrane of the chloroplast. The hydrogen ions which are pumped across the membrane diffuse through **ATP synthase**, resulting in the production of ATP. This process is shown in the following diagram.

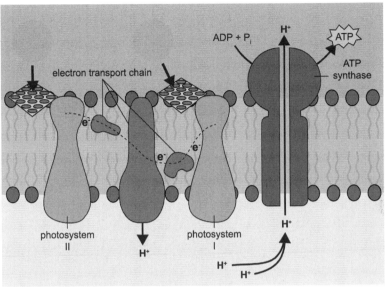

ATP synthesis in plants

4.3   Photoreceptor protein systems in animals

The following diagram shows the structure of the eye. This section will focus on two types of cells found in the retina (the tissue at the back of the eye which converts light into electrical signals).

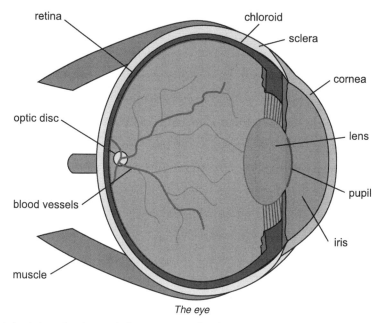

The eye

Animals have two types of photoreceptor cells within the retina of the eye; about 125 million rods and 6 million cones (named due to their shapes). These cells are shown in the following diagram.

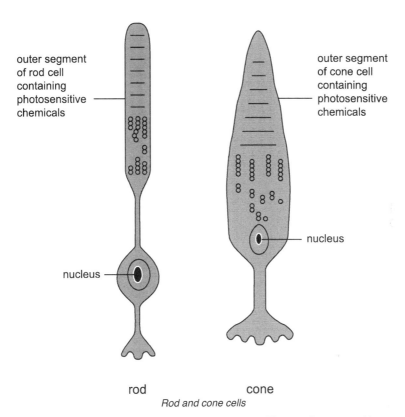

rod   cone
Rod and cone cells

Rod cells contain one type of light-sensitive pigment. These cells are sensitive to changes in light intensity and are particularly useful for vision in areas of low light intensity, e.g. a dim room. Nocturnal animals have a greater proportion of rod cells in their retina which gives them better vision at night.

Cone cells are not as sensitive to light as rod cells; however, they are particularly sensitive to specific colours (wavelengths) of light: green, red, blue and (in some animals) UV. Cone cells allow animals to have colour vision. People who are colour blind lack a particular type of cone cell in their retina.

Each rod or cone cell in the retina contains visual pigments that consist of a light-absorbing molecule, called **retinal**, that is bonded to a membrane protein, called **opsin**. In combination, opsin and retinal make up the visual pigment rhodopsin (as shown in the following diagram). In cone cells, different forms of opsin give sensitivity to specific wavelengths of light (red, green, blue or UV). In rod cells, the rhodopsin absorbs a wider range of wavelengths, and a greater degree of amplification from a single **photon** of light results in sensitivity at low light intensities.

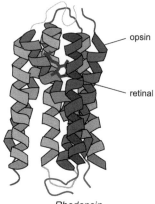

Rhodopsin

When stimulated by a photon of light, rhodopsin becomes excited and a nerve impulse may be generated:

*   excited rhodopsin activates **G-proteins** which, in turn, activate many enzyme molecules;

*   the enzyme molecules cause the closure of ion channels by catalysing the removal of molecules that keep channels open;

*   the inward leakage of positive ions (Na^+ and Ca^+) is halted so the membrane potential increases;

*   **hyperpolarisation** (increasing charge) stimulates a nerve impulse.

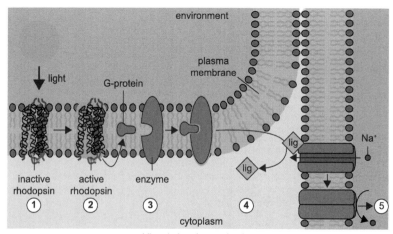

Visual signal transduction

1. A photon of light excites rhodopsin.

2. Excited rhodopsin activates G-proteins.

3. G-proteins activate enzyme molecules.

4. The enzyme removes the ligand from Na^+ channels.

5. The Na^+ channels close so the membrane potential increases; this hyperpolarisation stimulates a nerve impulse.

4.4   Learning points

Summary

- Photoreceptor protein systems are found across the three domains.

- In archaea, bacteriorhodopsin molecules generate potential differences by absorbing light to pump protons across the membrane. The resulting diffusion of hydrogen ions back across the membrane drives ATP synthase.

- In plants, the light absorbed by photosynthetic pigments within protein systems drives an electron flow that pumps hydrogen ions across the thylakoid membrane of the chloroplast. The resulting diffusion of hydrogen ions back across the membrane drives ATP synthase.

- In animals, the light-sensitive molecule retinal is combined with a membrane protein opsin (forming rhodopsin) and a cascade of proteins amplifies the signal.

- In cone cells, different forms of opsin give sensitivity to specific wavelengths of light (red, green, blue or UV).

- In rod cells, the rhodopsin absorbs a wider range of wavelengths, and a greater degree of amplification by the protein cascade results in sensitivity at low light intensities.

- When stimulated by a photon of light, rhodopsin becomes excited and a nerve impulse may be generated. Excited rhodopsin activates G-proteins which, in turn, activate many enzyme molecules. The enzyme molecules cause the closure of ion channels by catalysing the removal of molecules that keep channels open. The inward leakage of positive ions (Na^+ and Ca^+) is halted so the membrane potential increases. Hyperpolarisation (increasing charge) stimulates a nerve impulse.

4.5   End of topic test

End of Topic 4 test

Go online

Q1: What name is given to proteins which are capable of sensing and responding to light? *(1 mark)*

....

Q2: Which domains of life contain proteins capable of sensing and responding to light? *(1 mark)*

a) Archaea and eukaryotes
b) Archaea and prokaryotes
c) Eukaryotes and prokaryotes
d) Archaea, eukaryotes and prokaryotes

....

Q3: Bacteriorhodopsin molecules generate potential differences by absorbing light to pump _____ across the membrane. *(1 mark)*

....

Q4: After being pumped across the membrane, they return through _____, generating ATP. *(1 mark)*

....

Q5: Explain how absorption of light by photosynthetic pigments results in the generation of ATP. *(4 marks)*

....

© HERIOT-WATT UNIVERSITY

The following diagram shows the structure of rhodopsin.

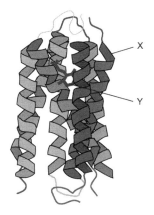

Q6: What does the letter X represent in the diagram? *(1 mark)*

....

Q7: What does the letter Y represent in the diagram? *(1 mark)*

....

Q8: What type of cell contains rhodopsin, which absorbs a wide range of wavelengths and provides sensitivity at low light intensities? *(1 mark)*

....

Q9: What type of molecule is activated when light stimulates rhodopsin? *(1 mark)*

....

....

Topic 5

Communication within multicellular organisms

Contents

Prerequisite knowledge

You should already know that:

- *hormones are chemical messengers;*

- *hormones are produced by endocrine glands and travel in the bloodstream to target tissues;*

- *target tissues have receptors which are complementary to a specific hormone;*

- *pancreatic receptors respond to high blood glucose levels by causing secretion of insulin;*

- *insulin brings about the conversion of glucose to glycogen in the liver, decreasing blood glucose concentration.*

Learning objectives

By the end of this topic, you should be able to:

- state that multicellular organisms achieve coordination through extracellular signalling molecules, receptors and responses;

- describe the role of receptor molecules on the cell surface;

- describe the effect of a ligand binding to receptor proteins;

- state that different cell types produce specific signals which can only be detected and responded to by cells with the specific receptor - in a multicellular organism, different cell types may show a tissue-specific response to the same signal;

- state that hydrophobic signals can be detected by receptor molecules in the nucleus and can directly influence transcription of genes;

- give examples of hydrophobic signalling molecules;

- explain how hydrophobic signalling molecules affect proteins in the nucleus;

- describe the role of the hormone thyroxine in controlling the transcription of the gene for Na/K-ATPase;

- state that peptide hormones and neurotransmitters are hydrophilic signalling molecules, and require receptor molecules to be at the surface of the cell;

- describe the role of transmembrane receptors in responding to hydrophilic signals;

- state that transduced hydrophilic signals often involve cascades of G-proteins or phosphorylation by kinase enzymes;

- describe the role of insulin with reference to the GLUT4 glucose transporter;

- describe the causes of Type 1 and Type 2 diabetes;

- state that exercise triggers recruitment of GLUT4 so can improve uptake of glucose to fat and muscle cells in subjects with Type 2 diabetes;

- describe the role of ADH with reference to the channel protein aquaporin 2 (AQP2).

5.1   Coordination

Multicellular organisms show division of labour, this means that different cells carry out different functions within defined areas of the body.

The cells of the body must be able to communicate with each other. They must be able to receive information from other parts of the body and act upon it. Multicellular organisms achieve coordination of communication by means of **extracellular** signalling molecules, receptors and responses. One tissue in the body will release a signalling molecule which will travel to another tissue with complementary receptors. This allows a signal to passed from one cell to another.

Receptor molecules of target cells are proteins with a binding site for a signal molecule. Binding changes the **conformation** of the receptor and this can alter the response of the cell.

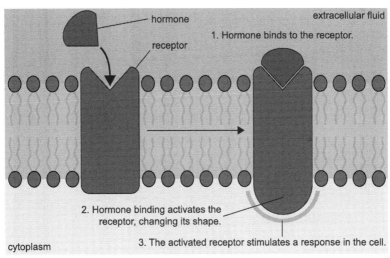

Signal reception

Different cell types produce specific signals which can only be detected and responded to by cells with the specific receptor. In a multicellular organism, different cell types may show a tissue-specific response to the same signal.

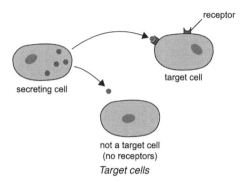

Target cells

When an extracellular signalling molecule (such as a hormone) binds to and activates a specific receptor, signal transduction occurs. The receptor may be located on the surface of the cell or inside the cell. Reception triggers a series of events inside the cell, resulting in a response, e.g. activation of an enzyme or G-protein, or the activation of proteins that regulate gene transcription.

Signal transduction pathway

Go online

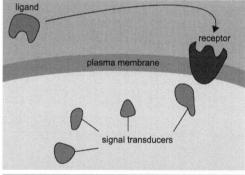

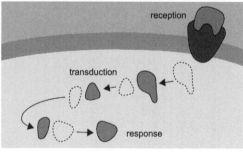

5.2 Hydrophobic signals and control of transcription

Hydrophobic signals

Hydrophobic signals can pass through membranes so their receptor molecules can be within the nucleus. They are able to do this because the tails of the phospholipids in the plasma membrane are also hydrophobic and allow the molecules to pass across. Hydrophobic signals can directly influence transcription of genes. The thyroid hormone thyroxine and steroid hormones are examples of hydrophobic signalling molecules.

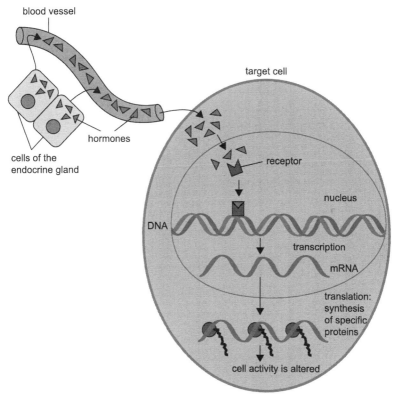

Hydrophobic signalling

Thyroxine

Thyroxine is a hydrophobic hormone produced by the thyroid gland. It is involved in regulating the rate of metabolism. Because it is hydrophobic, it can cross the plasma membrane of a cell and interact with proteins inside the cell.

When thyroxine is not present, its receptor protein binds onto the DNA in the nucleus. This inhibits the transcription of the gene for Na/K-ATPase (sodium-potassium pump). When thyroxine is present, the receptor protein undergoes a conformational change and can no longer bind the DNA; this allows transcription of the gene for Na/K-ATPase (sodium-potassium pump) to take place. Increased production of the Na/K-ATPase (sodium-potassium pump) results in an increase in metabolic rate.

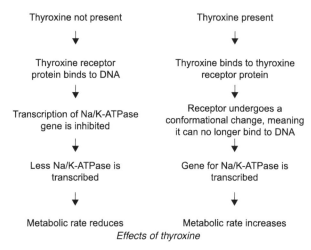

Effects of thyroxine

Steroid hormone

The receptor proteins for steroid hormones are transcription factors. A transcription factor is a protein which binds to DNA and controls the rate of transcription. Transcription factors can enhance or block the binding of RNA polymerase to specific genes, thereby controlling whether the gene is transcribed or not.

Steroid hormones, such as testosterone and oestrogen, are hydrophobic and can pass across the plasma membrane of target cells. When a steroid hormone signal binds to the receptor protein in the nucleus, the transcription factor is then able to bind to gene regulatory sequences of DNA and allow transcription to take place.

Steroid hormone passes across the plasma membrane
↓
The hormone binds to the receptor protein, activating it
↓
The activated receptor protein acts as a transcription
factor and binds to DNA
↓
The activated receptor protein (transcription factor)
brings about transcription of specific genes
Steroid hormone

Cell signalling: The action of testosterone

Go online

Q1: Complete the diagram by matching the labels to the gaps.

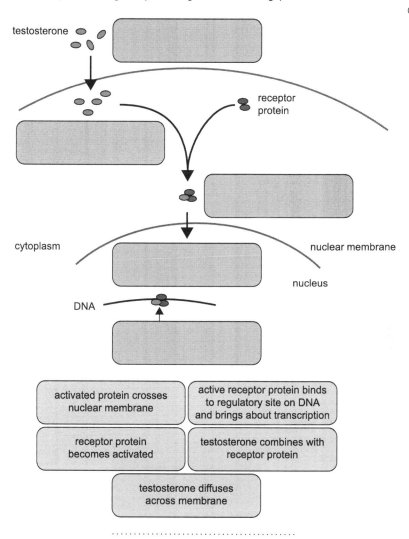

testosterone

receptor protein

cytoplasm

nuclear membrane

nucleus

DNA

activated protein crosses nuclear membrane

active receptor protein binds to regulatory site on DNA and brings about transcription

receptor protein becomes activated

testosterone combines with receptor protein

testosterone diffuses across membrane

5.3   Hydrophilic signals and transduction

Hydrophilic signals

Hydrophilic signals require receptor molecules to be at the surface of the cell because they are not capable of passing across the **hydrophobic** plasma membrane.

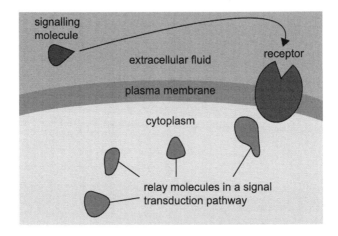

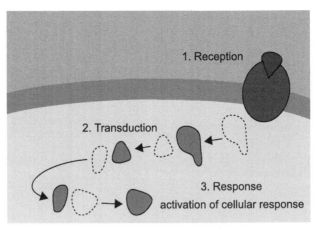

Hydrophilic signalling molecules

Stage 1 - reception

Transmembrane receptors change **conformation** (shape) when the **ligand** (signalling molecule) binds outside the cell. The signal molecule does not enter the cell, but the signal is transduced across the membrane of the cell.

Stage 2 - transduction

Receptor proteins convert an **extracellular** chemical signal to a specific **intracellular** response through a signal transduction pathway. Transduced hydrophilic signals often involve cascades of G-proteins or **phosphorylation** by kinase enzymes.

Transduction by G-proteins

G-protein-coupled receptors (GPCRs) are linked to a G-protein. The G-protein acts as a switch that is either on or off, depending on which of the two guanine nucleotides (GDP or GTP) is attached. When a hydrophilic signalling molecule binds to the extracellular side of a GPRC, a cascade of events is initiated.

Initially, when GDP is bound, the G-protein is inactive. On binding of a hydrophilic hormone to the receptor, GTP replaces GDP in the G-protein, and the G-protein becomes active. The active G-protein stimulates an enzyme, leading to a response in the cell. The response is only temporary because the G-protein also acts as a GTPase and soon hydrolyses the bound GTP into GDP, making the G-protein inactive again.

G-protein linked receptors

Go online

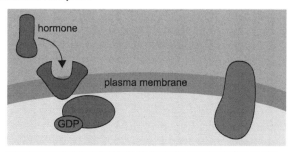

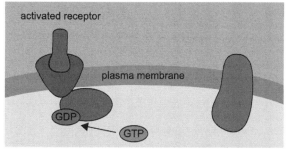

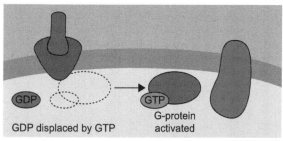

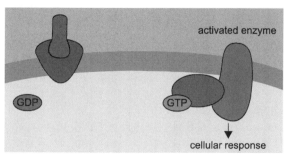

Transduction by phosphorylation

Receptor tyrosine kinases (RTKs) are transmembrane proteins. Their extracellular domain is capable of binding ligands (such as hydrophilic hormones) and their intracellular domain functions as a kinase enzyme. Kinase enzymes carry out phosphorylation reactions (addition of a phosphate group to substrates).

When a ligand binds to a RTK, tyrosine amino acids on the receptor become phosphorylated causing a conformational change in the receptor. This results in the kinase domains in the receptors becoming activated and phosphorylating downstream cytoplasmic molecules, resulting in various cellular responses.

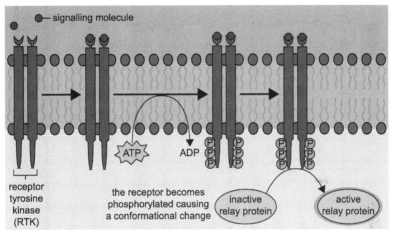

Transduction by phosphorylation

Stage 3 - response

The response of the cell will vary depending on the signal. For example, hormone binding may trigger recruitment of a channel protein to the surface of the cell. A hormone binding to a GPCR may result in the opening of an ion channel, while a hormone binding to a RTK may bring about transcription of certain genes. We are going to look at the action of two hydrophilic signalling molecules in more detail (insulin and ADH).

Insulin

The levels of glucose in the blood must be kept within strict limits. Hormones are involved in maintaining a constant blood glucose level. An increase in blood glucose concentration is detected by cells in the pancreas, which produce insulin. Insulin plays an important role in allowing fat tissue and skeletal muscles to absorb glucose from the bloodstream. Glucose passes into cells by travelling through transporter proteins in the plasma membrane (by facilitated diffusion).

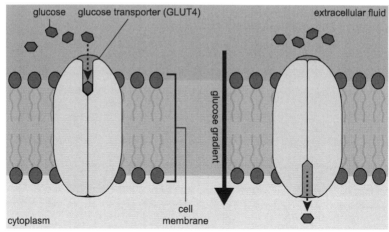

Glucose transport

Binding of the peptide hormone insulin to its receptor triggers recruitment of GLUT4 glucose transporters to the cell membrane of fat and muscle cells. GLUT4 transporters allow glucose to pass across the plasma and enter the cell.

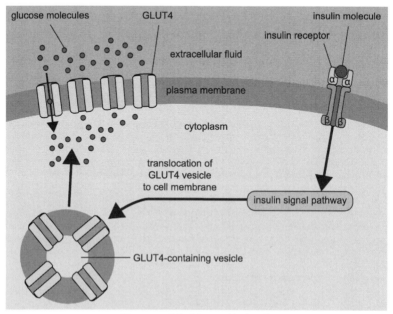

Glucose uptake triggered by insulin

In some individuals, there is a failure at some stage of the insulin signalling pathway. This results in a condition called diabetes. There are two type of diabetes.

- Type 1 - caused by a failure to produce insulin in the pancreas.

- Type 2 - caused by loss of insulin receptor function. This type of diabetes is usually associated with obesity.

Type 1 diabetes is treated with regular injections of insulin throughout the day. Type 2 diabetes may be treated with medications to lower blood glucose levels along with lifestyle changes, which may include consuming less sugar and increasing activity levels (this will aid weight loss if this is necessary). Exercise also triggers recruitment of GLUT4 so can improve uptake of glucose to fat and muscle cells in subjects with Type 2 diabetes.

Anti-diuretic hormone (ADH)

The kidney contains thousands of filtering units called nephrons.

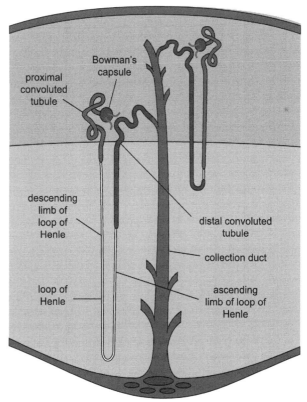

Nephron

In the nephron water, salts, urea and glucose are filtered out of the blood in the glomerulus (located within the Bowman's capsule). The substances filtered out (the glomerular filtrate) pass along the kidney tubule where all glucose, some water and some salts are reabsorbed. The remaining urea, water and salts form urine which passes down the collecting duct.

The signalling molecule anti-diuretic hormone (ADH) affects the rate of water reabsorption in the nephron. ADH is a hydrophilic peptide hormone which acts on the collecting ducts of the nephron. When ADH binds to receptors on the cells of the collecting ducts, a signal transduction process occurs which results in the recruitment of the channel protein aquaporin 2 (AQP2) to the membrane of the cells. Aquaporins provide a highly efficient route for water to move across membranes.

When water levels in the body are low, the pituitary gland releases ADH which travels in the bloodstream to the collecting ducts of the nephrons in the kidneys. The binding of ADH to its receptor results in an increased number of AQP2 channels in the membrane of the collecting duct cell. This increases the reabsorption of water and a small volume of concentrated urine is produced. If water levels within the body increase, less ADH is released by the pituitary gland. This results in less water being reabsorbed in the nephrons and a large volume of dilute urine is produced. This negative feedback control mechanism involving the recruitment of AQP2 allows control of water balance in terrestrial vertebrates.

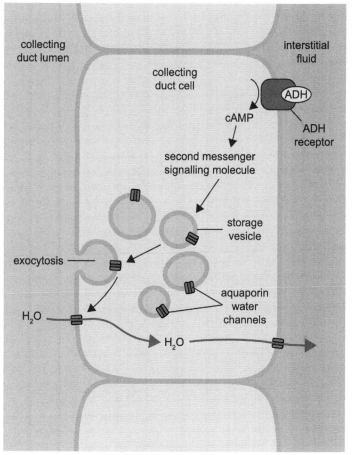

Action of ADH

In diabetes insipidus, ADH fails to properly regulate the level of water within the body. Diabetes insipidus is caused by a failure to produce ADH or insensitivity of its receptor. Diabetes insipidus causes severe thirst due to over production of dilute urine. Desmopressin is often prescribed to treat the condition. Desmopressin is a manufactured (and more powerful) version of ADH.

© HERIOT-WATT UNIVERSITY

5.4 Learning points

Summary

- Multicellular organisms achieve coordination through extracellular signalling molecules, receptors and responses.

- Receptor molecules of target cells are proteins with a binding site for a signal molecule.

- Binding changes the conformation of the receptor and this can alter the response of the cell.

- Different cell types produce specific signals which can only be detected and responded to by cells with the specific receptor; in a multicellular organism, different cell types may show a tissue-specific response to the same signal.

- Hydrophobic signals can be detected by receptor molecules in the nucleus.

- Hydrophobic signalling molecules include steroid hormones and the thyroid hormone thyroxine.

- Hydrophobic signals can pass through membranes so their receptor molecules can be within the nucleus and they can directly influence transcription of genes.

- Thyroxine receptor protein binds to DNA in the absence of thyroxine and inhibits transcription of the gene for Na/K-ATPase - when thyroxine binds to the receptor protein, conformational change prevents the protein binding to the DNA, allowing transcription of the gene for Na/KATPase, resulting in an increase in metabolic rate;

- The receptor proteins for steroid hormones (for example the sex hormones) are transcription factors; only once the hormone signal has bound to the receptor can the transcription factor bind to gene regulatory sequences of DNA which allow transcription to occur.

- Peptide hormones and neurotransmitters are hydrophilic signalling molecules.

- Hydrophilic signals require receptor molecules to be at the surface of the cell.

- Transmembrane receptors change conformation when the ligand binds outside the cell; the signal molecule does not enter the cell, but the signal is transduced across the membrane of the cell.

- Transduced hydrophilic signals often involve cascades of G-proteins or phosphorylation by kinase enzymes.

- Binding of the peptide hormone insulin to its receptor triggers recruitment of GLUT4 glucose transporters to the cell membrane of fat and muscle cells - this facilitates the uptake of glucose into the cells.

> **Summary continued**
>
> - Type 1 diabetes is caused by a lack of insulin production, whereas type 2 diabetes is caused by loss of insulin receptor function.
>
> - Exercise triggers recruitment of GLUT4 so can improve uptake of glucose to fat and muscle cells in subjects with Type 2 diabetes.
>
> - Binding of the peptide hormone ADH to its receptor in the collecting duct of the kidney triggers recruitment of the channel protein aquaporin 2 (AQP2).
>
> - Aquaporins provide a highly efficient route for water to move across membranes.
>
> - Recruitment of AQP2 allows control of water balance in terrestrial vertebrates.
>
> - Failure to produce ADH or insensitivity of its receptor results in diabetes insipidus.

5.5 Extended response question

The activity which follows presents an extended response question similar to the style that you will encounter in the examination.

You should have a good understanding of cell signalling before attempting the question.

You should give your completed answer to your teacher or tutor for marking, or try to mark it yourself using the suggested marking scheme.

Extended response question: Cell signalling

Give an account of cell signalling. *(8 marks)*

. . . .

5.6   End of topic test

Go online

End of Topic 5 test

Q2: Which of the following describes how genes that increase metabolic rate are activated by a hydrophobic signalling molecule? *(1 mark)*

a) The hormone thyroxine binds to a receptor protein on DNA and stops it inhibiting transcription.

b) The hormone thyroxine binds to a receptor protein in the cytoplasm and the complex regulates transcription.

c) The hormone testosterone binds to a receptor protein on DNA and stops it inhibiting transcription.

d) The hormone testosterone binds to a receptor protein in the cytoplasm and the complex regulates transcription.

....

Q3: Where are the receptors for hydrophobic signalling molecules located? *(1 mark)*

....

Q4: To which group of hormones does oestrogen belong? *(1 mark)*

....

Q5: Where are the receptors for hydrophilic signalling molecules located? *(1 mark)*

....

Q6: Where are the target cells for ADH located? *(1 mark)*

....

Q7: Name the channel protein recruited to the membrane as a result of ADH binding to its receptor. *(1 mark)*

....

Q8: Name the condition caused by a lack of ADH production. *(1 mark)*

....

Q9: Describe the effect of insulin binding to its receptor. *(2 marks)*

....

Topic 6

Protein control of cell division

Contents

Prerequisite knowledge

You should already know that:

- *mitosis is required for growth and repair;*

- *the sequence of events of mitosis (including the terms chromatids, equator and spindle fibres);*

- *diploid cells have two matching sets of chromosomes, which are replicated during mitosis.*

Learning objectives

By the end of this topic, you should be able to:

- *describe the composition and role of the cytoskeleton;*

- *describe the role of microtubules within the cytoskeleton;*

- *describe the stages of the cell cycle;*

- *state that an uncontrolled reduction in the rate of the cell cycle may result in degenerative disease, and an uncontrolled increase in the rate of the cell cycle may result in tumour formation;*

- *describe the stages of interphase, including G1, S and G2 stages;*

- *describe the stages of mitosis, including prophase, metaphase, anaphase and telophase;*

- *describe the role of spindle fibres in the movement of chromosomes on metaphase plate, separation of sister chromatids and formation of daughter nuclei;*

- *describe the process of cytokinesis;*

- *describe the role of checkpoints throughout the cell cycle;*

- *state which checkpoint is the most important for many cells;*

- *explain why a cell may enter G0 phase after G1;*

- *describe the formation and role of cyclin dependent kinases (CDKs);*

- *describe the role of retinoblastoma (Rb) protein;*

- *describe the role of p53 protein in controlling the cell cycle;*

- *state that programmed cell death (apoptosis) is triggered by cell death signals which activate inactive forms of DNAase and proteinases (collectively known as caspases) that destroy the cell;*

- *state that the destruction of cells must be carefully controlled in a multicellular organism;*

- *describe intrinsic and extrinsic signals which may lead to apoptosis.*

6.1 The cytoskeleton

The **eukaryotic** cell is a three-dimensional structure. It has a network of proteins extending throughout the cytoplasm, known as the cytoskeleton. The cytoskeleton is anchored to proteins in the plasma membrane and is dynamic in nature, constantly breaking down and re-forming. The function of the cytoskeleton is to:

- provide mechanical support so that the cell maintains its shape;

- provide anchorage for many organelles and some enzymes;

- enable the whole cell to move;

- enable organelles within the cell to move.

The following image shows two proteins of the cytoskeleton, microtubules are marked green and actin filaments are marked red.

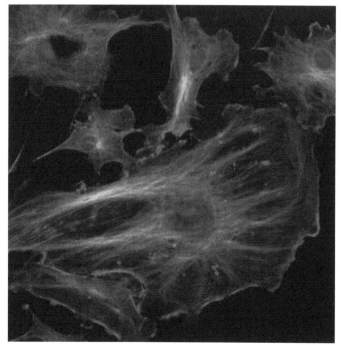

The cytoskeleton

The cytoskeleton is made up of different types of protein including microfilaments, intermediate filaments and microtubules. Microfilaments are the smallest filaments of the cytoskeleton and include the protein actin. Intermediate filaments are slightly larger than microfilaments and have a similar role in maintaining cell shape. Microtubules are hollow, straight cylinders composed of globular proteins called tubulins. The microtubule itself is made up of alternating dimers of α and β tubulin. Microtubules govern the location and movement of membrane-bound organelles and other cell components.

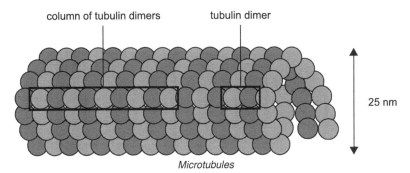

Microtubules

Microtubules are found in all eukaryotic cells and originate from the centrosome (microtubule organising centre (MTOC)). The centrosome is found near the nucleus and contains centrioles, which are the site of microtubule synthesis within the centrosome. Microtubules play an important role in cell division as this process requires remodelling of the cell's cytoskeleton. Microtubules also form the spindle fibres, which are active during cell division. The following image shows a cell which is dividing; the microtubules of the spindle fibres are marked green and the chromosomes are marked blue.

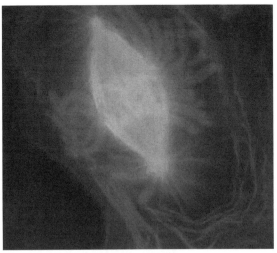

A cell undergoing mitosis

6.2   Cell cycle

Cell division allows organisms to grow and develop, to replace dead cells and repair tissue. As the term 'cell cycle' suggests, this is a continual process, but it can be divided up into distinct stages. The whole cycle can be divided up into two parts.

1. Interphase.

2. The mitotic phase.

Interphase lasts much longer than the mitotic phase. When we look at a group of cells by light microscopy, only a small proportion of them are in the mitotic phase; most of them appear to be doing nothing. Although we cannot see anything taking place, describing interphase as the 'resting phase' is in fact far from reality. Interphase is an active period of growth. During interphase, protein synthesis takes place, cytoplasmic organelles are synthesised, the cell grows and replicates its chromosomes.

Interphase is divided into three sub-phases.

1. G1 is the first 'gap' phase; it is a growth period where proteins and organelles are synthesised.

2. During S phase the cell continues to grow and copies its chromosomes in preparation for mitosis.

3. The final phase is G2 (the second 'gap' phase); this is another growth period during which proteins and organelles are synthesised.

At the end of G2, cells enter the mitotic phase (M), which is divided up into two stages.

1. Mitosis - when the nucleus and its contents divide.

2. Cytokinesis - the separation of the cytoplasm into daughter cells.

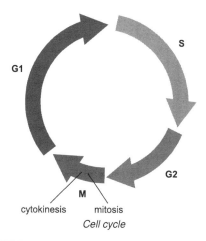

Cell cycle

An uncontrolled reduction in the rate of the cell cycle may result in degenerative disease. For example, alteration in the normal control of cell cycle is thought to lead to expression of certain proteins associated with Alzheimer's disease, eventually resulting in neuronal cell death. An uncontrolled increase in the rate of the cell cycle may result in tumour formation. The cell cycle must, therefore, be tightly controlled.

Mitosis

Mitosis is broken up into four stages that can be distinguished using a light microscope. Each stage progresses to the next as a continual process. At the end of interphase, cells enter prophase.

1. Prophase

   - Chromatin starts to condense into discrete chromosomes. Each duplicated chromosome appears as two identical sister chromatids joined at the centromere.
   - In the cytoplasm, the mitotic spindle begins to form between the two centrosomes. This process pushes the centrosomes away from each other along the surface of the nucleus.
   - At the end of prophase, cells enter metaphase.

2. Metaphase

   - In the initial stage (prometaphase), the nuclear membrane breaks up. Bundles of microtubules extend from each pole toward the equator of the cell, and attach to the centromere of each chromatid.
   - As the cell enters metaphase, the centrosomes are now at opposite poles of the cell.
   - The chromosomes line up on the metaphase plate in the middle of the cell. The term metaphase plate is used to describe the arrangement of the chromosomes at the equator of the cell.
   - Each of the sister chromatids in each chromosome is attached to microtubules from opposite ends of the parent cell at a point called the **kinetochore**.
   - At the end of metaphase, cells enter anaphase.

3. Anaphase

   - The paired centromeres of each chromosome separate and the chromatids begin moving apart as the spindle shortens. The poles also move further apart. Each chromatid can now be called a chromosome.
   - By the end of anaphase, the two poles of the cell each have an identical and complete set of chromosomes.
   - At the end of anaphase, cells enter telophase.

4. Telophase

   - The cell lengthens during telophase and a nuclear membrane forms around each set of chromosomes. The chromosomes start to uncoil.
   - Cytokinesis also takes place during this period, which involves the separation of the cytoplasm into two daughter cells.

Mitosis

Q1: Complete the diagram using the labels provided.

Go online

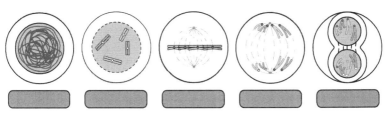

Labels: anaphase, interphase, metaphase, prophase, telophase.

....

Microtubules play an important role throughout this process. The spindle begins to form at prophase and is organised by the centrosomes at the two poles of the cell. The spindle fibres allow both the alignment of the chromosomes at the metaphase plate and the separation of chromatids to opposite poles. The spindle fibres also play an important role in the formation of daughter nuclei, allowing the separated chromatids to group at the opposite poles of the cell.

(a)   (b)

(c)   (d)

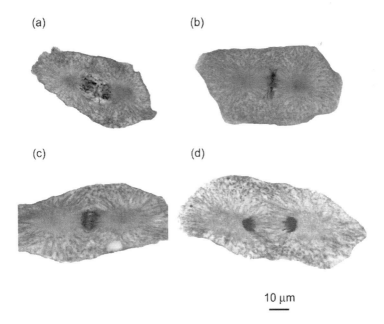

10 μm

Phases of mitosis; (a) prophase; (b) metaphase; (c) early anaphase; (d) telophase

6.3   Control of the cell cycle

Cell cycle checkpoints

The timing and rate of cell division is crucial to normal growth, development and maintenance of tissues. Frequency of division will vary with cell type. For example, human skin cells divide throughout life, whereas liver cells will only divide if the need arises (for example, as a result of injury). In a mature adult, nerve cells do not divide at all.

The cell cycle must be controlled to ensure that events in the cell cycle proceed in the correct order and that each event is completed before the next starts. For example, it would be catastrophic for the cell if it entered M phase before the chromosomes had duplicated in S phase. Sufficient nutrients and growth factors must also be present before the cell commits itself to the next stage in the cell cycle.

There are checkpoint at various stages within the cell cycle. This is where stop and start signals regulate the cycle. Checkpoints register internal and external cell signals that report whether crucial processes up to that point have been completed successfully or not, and whether the cycle should proceed. There are three major checkpoints in the cell cycle.

1. G1 checkpoint - occurs towards the end of G1; sufficient cell growth must have occurred and other conditions must be satisfied before the cell can enter S phase.

2. G2 checkpoint - occurs at the end of G2; DNA replication must be completed for the cell cycle to continue.

3. M checkpoint - occurs during metaphase and controls entry to anaphase. The M checkpoint checks that chromosomes are aligned correctly on the metaphase plate and, therefore, ensures that each daughter cell receives the correct number of chromosomes.

In many mammalian cells, the G1 checkpoint appears to be the most important. If a cell receives the 'go ahead' signal at this checkpoint, it will usually complete the cycle and divide. If not, it will exit the cycle and switch to a non-dividing state called the G0 phase. At any one time, most somatic cells are in the G0 phase. During the G0 phase, the cell is not dividing or preparing to divide; it is known as a quiescent (non-proliferating) phase.

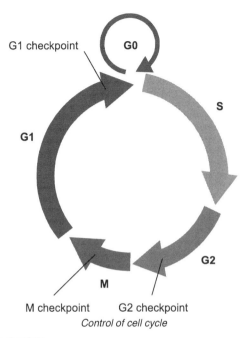

G1 checkpoint   G0

S

G1

G2

M

M checkpoint   G2 checkpoint

Control of cell cycle

Proteins at checkpoints

The control of the cell cycle is a complex process which involves many regulatory proteins. Whether a cell 'passes' a checkpoint or not is dependent upon a series of factors involving proteins. As the cell size increases during G1, cyclin proteins accumulate and combine with kinases to form regulatory protein molecules which are known as cyclin-dependent kinases (CDKs). CDKs cause the phosphorylation of proteins that stimulate the cell cycle. If a sufficient threshold of phosphorylation is reached, the cell cycle moves on to the next stage. If an insufficient threshold is reached, the cell is held at a checkpoint.

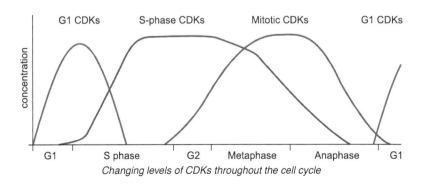

Changing levels of CDKs throughout the cell cycle

Retinoblastoma (Rb) is a cell cycle regulatory protein. The non-phosphorylated form of Rb restricts progression from G1 phase into S phase. It acts by binding to a transcription factor, therefore preventing transcription of certain genes required for S phase to begin; thus the cell remains in G1.

When a cell is about to enter S phase, the G1 CDKs phosphorylate the retinoblastoma protein. Phosphorylation inhibits the activity of Rb, meaning that it can no longer bind the transcription factor. The transcription factor is released and brings about transcription of the genes that are required to initiate DNA replication, allowing the cell to enter S phase.

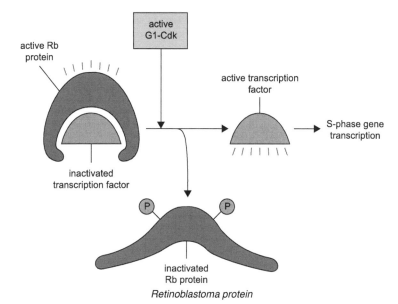

Retinoblastoma protein

Cell cycle checkpoints can also assess damage to a cell's DNA and prevent it from continuing the cell cycle. DNA damage triggers the activation of several proteins that can stimulate DNA repair, arrest the cell cycle or cause cell death. One of the proteins activated as a result of DNA damage is p53. The p53 protein has been described as "the guardian of the genome" because of its role in maintaining a functional genome. The fact that the majority of human cancers can be linked to mutations in the p53 gene demonstrates the importance of this protein in regulating cell cycle.

Upon recognising damage to the DNA of the cell, p53 can bring about several cellular responses:

- it can activate DNA repair proteins to repair the DNA damage;

- it can arrest the cell cycle at the G1 checkpoint, which means that the cell cycle halts at this point - this can allow DNA repair proteins time to recognise and fix the DNA damage so the cell can restart the cell cycle;

- if the DNA damage is too severe, it can initiate apoptosis (programmed cell death).

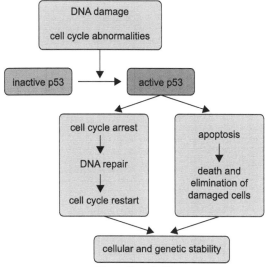

The action of p53

6.4   Control of apoptosis

The destruction of cells must be carefully controlled in a multicellular organism. The destruction of cells is brought about by a process known as programmed cell death or **apoptosis**. Apoptosis is an important process throughout the growth and development of an organism. For example, during human embryonic development, programmed cell death of the cells between the fingers and toes allows individual digits to form (rather than webbed digits). Apoptosis also has implications in the development of certain diseases; excessive apoptosis may result in degenerative conditions, while inhibition of apoptosis may result in tumour formation or cancer.

Apoptosis is triggered by cell death signals which result in the activation of DNAases and a variety of **proteinases** (collectively known as **caspases**). DNAases catalyse the breakdown of DNA by hydrolysing phosphodiester bonds of the backbone, and proteinases bring about degradation of cellular proteins. The combined action of DNAases and proteinases destroys the cell. The cell fragments produced by apoptosis (known as apoptotic bodies) are engulfed and destroyed by **phagocytes**.

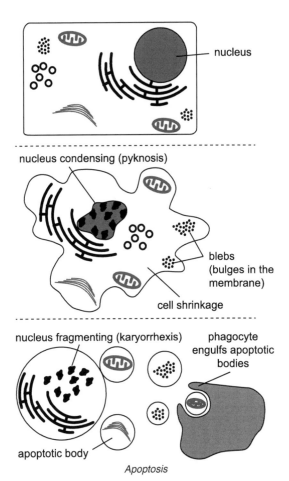

Apoptosis

Cell death signals may originate outwith the cell (extrinsic signals), for example from **lymphocytes**. Cytotoxic T-lymphocytes express a death activator ligand on their surface called Fas. When a cell death ligand such as Fas binds to its surface receptor protein on a target cell, it activates a protein cascade that produces active caspases. The activated caspases then bring about apoptosis.

Death signals may also originate within the cell (intrinsic signals). For example, as a result of DNA damage, the presence of p53 protein can activate a caspase cascade. In the absence of cell growth factors, cells may also initiate apoptosis.

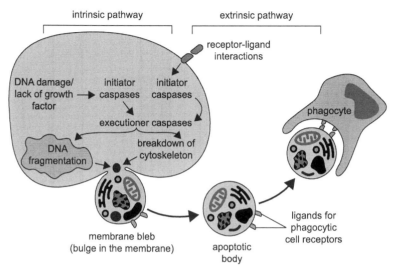

Intrinsic and extrinsic apoptosis pathways

6.5   Learning points

┌─ Summary ──

- The cytoskeleton gives mechanical support and shape to cells. It consists of different types of proteins extending throughout the cytoplasm.

- Microtubules are composed of hollow, straight rods made of globular proteins called tubulins; they govern the location and movement of membrane-bound organelles and other cell components.

- Microtubules are found in all eukaryotic cells and radiate from the centrosome (the microtubule organising centre); they form the spindle fibres, which are active during cell division.

- Cell division requires the remodelling of the cell's cytoskeleton.

- The cell cycle regulates the growth and replacement of genetically identical cells throughout the life of the organism.

- An uncontrolled reduction in the rate of the cell cycle may result in degenerative disease, while an uncontrolled increase in the rate of the cell cycle may result in tumour formation.

- Cell cycle can be split into two main stages: the first phase is interphase and the second is the mitotic phase.

- Interphase is divided into three sub-phases: G1 is the first 'gap' phase - it is a growth period where proteins and organelles are synthesised; during S phase the cell continues to grow and DNA replication takes place; the final phase is G2 (the second 'gap' phase) - this is another growth period during which proteins and organelles are synthesised.

- Mitosis is broken up into four stages: prophase, metaphase, anaphase and telophase.

- During prophase, each duplicated chromosome appears as two identical sister chromatids which are joined at the centromere. In the cytoplasm, the mitotic spindle begins to form between the two centrosomes.

- During metaphase, the chromosomes line up on the metaphase plate in the middle of the cell. Each of the sister chromatids in each chromosome is attached to microtubules from opposite ends of the parent cell at a point called the kinetochore.

- During anaphase, the paired centromeres of each chromosome separate and the chromatids begin moving apart as the spindle shortens.

- During telophase, the cell lengthens and a nuclear membrane forms around each set of chromosomes. The chromosomes start to uncoil.

- Cytokinesis takes place during telophase, which involves the separation of the cytoplasm into two daughter cells.

Summary continued

- Spindle fibres play an important role in the movement of chromosomes on metaphase plate, separation of sister chromatids and formation of daughter nuclei.

- Checkpoints are critical control points where stop and go signals regulate the cycle; there are three checkpoints in the cell cycle: G1, G2 and M.

- For many cells, the G1 checkpoint is the most important. If a go ahead signal is not reached at the G1 checkpoint, the cell switches to a non-dividing state called the G0 phase.

- As the cell size increases during G1, cyclin proteins accumulate and combine with kinases to form regulatory protein molecules known as cyclin-dependent kinases (CDKs). CDKs cause the phosphorylation of proteins that stimulate the cell cycle.

- If a sufficient threshold of phosphorylation is reached, the cell cycle moves on to the next stage. If an insufficient threshold is reached, the cell is held at a checkpoint.

- The G1 Cdk phosphorylates a transcription factor inhibitor, retinoblastoma (Rb) protein, which allows DNA replication in the S phase.

- DNA damage triggers the activation of several proteins, including p53 which can stimulate DNA repair, arrest the cell cycle or cause cell death.

- Programmed cell death (apoptosis) is triggered by cell death signals which activate inactive forms of DNAase and proteinases (collectively known as caspases) that destroy the cell.

- Cell death signals may originate outwith the cell (for example from lymphocytes) and bind to a surface receptor protein to activate a protein cascade that produces active caspases.

- Death signals may also originate within the cell, for example, as a result of DNA damage, the presence of p53 protein can activate a caspase cascade.

- In the absence of cell growth factors, cells may also initiate apoptosis.

6.6   Extended response question

The activity which follows presents an extended response question similar to the style that you will encounter in the examination.

You should have a good understanding of the control of apoptosis before attempting the question.

You should give your completed answer to your teacher or tutor for marking, or try to mark it yourself using the suggested marking scheme.

Extended response question: Control of apoptosis

Describe the control of apoptosis. *(8 marks)*

. . . .

6.7   End of topic test

Go online

End of Topic 6 test

Q2:   The cytoskeleton is composed of: *(1 mark)*

a)   carbohydrate.
b)   lipid.
c)   nucleic acid.
d)   protein.

. . . .

Q3:   All eukaryotic cells have microtubules.   These are hollow rods constructed of columns of a protein called _____. *(1 mark)*

. . . .

Q4:   In animal cells, microtubules radiate out from a region near the nucleus called the _____. *(1 mark)*

. . . .

The following diagram illustrates the four phases of the cell cycle as arrows. One of the cell cycle events, cytokinesis, is indicated.

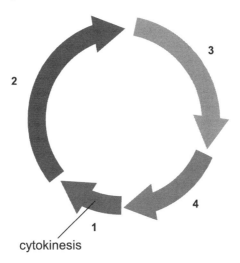

cytokinesis

Q5: Which of the following correctly lists the phases of the cell cycle in order? *(1 mark)*

a) G1, S, G2, M
b) M, G1, S, G2
c) M, G2, S, G1
d) G1, M, G2, S

. . . .

Q6: Identify the stage of mitosis illustrated by the following diagram. *(1 mark)*

a) Anaphase
b) Metaphase
c) Prophase
d) Telophase

. . . .

Q7: Identify the stage of mitosis illustrated by the following diagram. *(1 mark)*

a) Anaphase
b) Metaphase
c) Prophase
d) Telophase

. . . .

Q8: Identify the stage of mitosis illustrated by the following diagram. *(1 mark)*

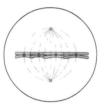

a) Anaphase
b) Metaphase
c) Prophase
d) Telophase

. . . .

Q9: Identify the stage of mitosis illustrated by the following diagram. *(1 mark)*

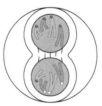

a) Anaphase
b) Metaphase
c) Prophase
d) Telophase

....

Q10: A cell that passes the checkpoint towards the end of G1 will probably: *(1 mark)*

a) have just completed cytokinesis.
b) move directly into G0.
c) move directly into M phase.
d) undergo chromosomal duplication.

....

Q11: Which of the following checkpoints is most important for a cell? *(1 mark)*

a) G1
b) G2
c) M

....

Q12: Describe the role of cyclin dependent kinases. *(1 mark)*

....

Q13: Name the protein that is activated by DNA damage which can stimulate DNA repair. *(1 mark)*

....

Q14: What is the collective term for proteinases activated during apoptosis? *(1 mark)*

....

Q15: Give an example of a cell death signal which originates from within the cell. *(1 mark)*

....

Q16: Give one reason why cell death must be carefully controlled in a multicellular organism. *(1 mark)*

....

....

© HERIOT-WATT UNIVERSITY

Topic 7

End of unit test

End of Unit 1 test

Laboratory techniques for biologists

Go online

Q1:   All scientists working in a laboratory have a responsibility to conform to health and safety legislation to minimise potential harm as a result of their work. For example, many scientists wear lab coats and safety glasses while performing experiments. What name is given to control measures which involve equipment such as lab coats? *(1 mark)*

....

Q2:   What piece of equipment can be used to quantify the concentration of a pigmented compound? *(1 mark)*

....

Q3:   Use the following standard curve estimate the protein concentration of a sample with an absorbance of 0.75. *(1 mark)*

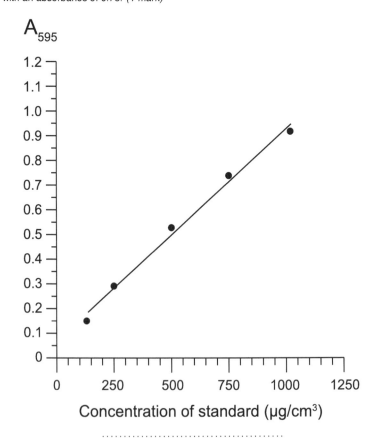

....

Q4: To produce stocks of a particular antibody, hybridomas must first be produced. Which two cell types are fused to produce hybridomas? *(1 mark)*

....

Q5: Antibodies can be used to detect the presence of a particular protein in a sample. How is binding between the antibody and target protein detected? *(1 mark)*

....

Q6: What is a haemocytometer used for? *(1 mark)*

....

Q7: What substance, containing growth factors, must be added to culture medium for successful growth of animal cells? *(1 mark)*

....

Q8: Why are aseptic techniques used when performing cell culture? *(1 mark)*

....

Proteomics, proteins structure, binding and conformational change

Q9: What name is given to the entire set of proteins expressed by a genome? *(1 mark)*

....

Q10: What type of bonds link the amino acids together in a protein? *(1 mark)*

....

Q11: What type of bonding is involved the secondary structure of a protein? *(1 mark)*

....

Q12: What aspects of secondary structure of proteins can be seen in the following diagram of myoglobin? *(1 mark)*

....

Q13: What aspects of tertiary structure of proteins can be seen in the diagram? *(1 mark)*

....

Q14: What factor determines the location of a protein within a cell? *(1 mark)*

....

Q15: Strong hydrophobic interactions hold _____ proteins within the phospholipid bilayer. *(1 mark)*

....

Q16: _____ proteins have fewer hydrophobic R groups interacting with the phospholipids. *(1 mark)*

....

Q17: Explain how DNA is able to bind to histone proteins. *(1 mark)*

....

Q18: Describe the induced fit model of enzyme action. *(1 mark)*

....

Q19: What name is given to the process whereby changes in binding at one subunit of a protein alter the affinity of the remaining subunits? *(1 mark)*

....

Q20: What type of enzyme is responsible for phosphorylation of other proteins? *(1 mark)*

....

Membrane proteins

Q21: What term is used to describe the passage of molecules through channel proteins? *(1 mark)*

. . . .

Q22: Conformational change in active transport requires energy from hydrolysis of _____. *(1 mark)*

. . . .

Q23: What type of channel is shown in the following diagram? *(1 mark)*

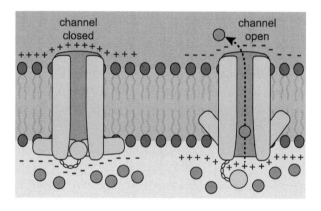

. . . .

Q24: Some cell surface receptor proteins convert an extracellular chemical signal to a specific intracellular response through a signal transduction pathway. Describe one intracellular response which may be brought about as a result of signal transduction. *(1 mark)*

. . . .

Q25: Which of the following is not a function of Na/KATPase (sodium-potassium pump)? *(1 mark)*

a) Generation of adenosine triphosphate (ATP).
b) Generation of ion gradient in kidney tubules.
c) Maintaining the ion gradient for resting potential in neurons.
d) Maintaining the osmotic balance in animal cells.

. . . .

Q26: Which of the following correctly describes the action of the Na/KATPase? *(1 mark)*

a) Two sodium ions out of the cell, three potassium ions into the cell.
b) Three sodium ions out of the cell, two potassium ions into the cell.
c) Two sodium ions into the cell, three potassium ions out of the cell.
d) Three sodium ions into the cell, two potassium ions out of the cell.

. . . .

Q27: Nerve transmission is a wave of _____ of the resting potential of a neuron. *(1 mark)*

. . . .

Q28: Describe the role of ligand-gated ion channels in the transmission of nerve impulses. *(3 marks)*

. . . .

Detecting and amplifying an environmental stimulus

Q29: Which type of ion is pumped across membranes by bacteriorhodopsin? *(1 mark)*

. . . .

Q30: Name the enzyme which allows these ions to return back across the membrane and bring about the production of ATP. *(1 mark)*

. . . .

Q31: Name the light sensitive molecule found within rhodopsin. *(1 mark)*

. . . .

Q32: Describe one cellular response which occurs as a result of rhodopsin becoming excited by a photon of light. *(1 mark)*

. . . .

Q33: Which statement below correctly describes features of cone cells in humans? *(1 mark)*

a) Cone cells do not function in low light intensity and contain different forms of opsins.
b) Cone cells function in low light intensity and contain different forms of opsins.
c) Cone cells do not function in low light intensity and do not contain different forms of opsins.
d) Cone cells function in low light intensity and do not contain different forms of opsins.

. . . .

Communication within multicellular organisms

Q34: What happens to a receptor protein when a signal molecule binds? *(1 mark)*

....

Q35: Why can the receptors for hydrophobic signalling molecules be within the nucleus? *(1 mark)*

....

Q36: Which statement below correctly describes the role of thyroxine? *(1 mark)*

a) Thyroxine brings about phosphorylation of intracellular proteins.
b) Thyroxine brings about transcription of the gene for Na/K-ATPase.
c) Thyroxine triggers activation of a cascade of G proteins.
d) Thyroxine triggers recruitment of GLUT4 to the cell membrane of fat and muscle cells.

....

Q37: What are the receptor proteins for steroid hormones? *(1 mark)*

....

Q38: Describe the cause of type 2 diabetes. *(1 mark)*

....

Q39: Explain why exercise may improve glucose uptake in patients with type 2 diabetes. *(1 mark)*

....

Q40: Describe the effect of ADH binding to its receptor. *(1 mark)*

....

Q41: What condition can be caused by a failure to produce ADH? *(1 mark)*

....

Protein control of cell division

The following diagram represents the phases of the cell cycle.

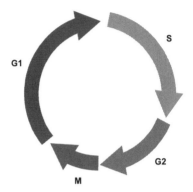

Q42: During which phase of the cell cycle are the chromosomes copied? *(1 mark)*

a) G1
b) S
c) G2
d) M

....

Q43: It is important that the rate of the cell cycle is carefully controlled. What type of disease may occur if there is a decrease in the rate? *(1 mark)*

....

Q44: Which stage of mitosis is described as follows? *(1 mark)*

Chromosomes line up at the equator of the cell. Each of the sister chromatids in each chromosome is attached to microtubules from opposite ends of the parent cell.

a) Anaphase
b) Metaphase
c) Prophase
d) Telophase

....

Q45: Which stage of mitosis is described as follows? *(1 mark)*

The cell lengthens and a nuclear membrane forms around each set of chromosomes. The chromosomes start to uncoil.

a) Anaphase
b) Metaphase
c) Prophase
d) Telophase

....

Q46: Which stage of mitosis is described as follows? *(1 mark)*

Duplicated chromosomes appears as two identical sister chromatids joined at the centromere. In the cytoplasm, the mitotic spindle begins to form between the two centrosomes.

a) Anaphase
b) Metaphase
c) Prophase
d) Telophase

....

Q47: Which stage of mitosis is described as follows? *(1 mark)*

Paired centromeres of each chromosome separate and the chromatids begin moving apart as the spindle shortens.

a) Anaphase
b) Metaphase
c) Prophase
d) Telophase

....

Q48: During the cell cycle, sufficient phosphorylation by G1 cyclin-dependent kinases allows: *(1 mark)*

a) DNA replication to occur.
b) the cell to arrest the cell cycle.
c) the cell to enter the mitotic phase.
d) the cell to repair DNA damage.

....

Q49: Microtubules play an important role in mitosis. Which structures, required for mitosis, are composed of microtubules? *(1 mark)*

....

Q50: Describe the role of CDKs. *(1 mark)*

....

Q51: Describe one role of p53 protein. *(1 mark)*

....

Q52: Give one example of an event that would trigger an intrinsic cell death signal. *(1 mark)*

....

Problem solving

A compound known as arsenic trioxide (ATO) has proved to be an effective treatment for some forms of leukaemia, but has little impact in treating solid tumours such as hepatocellular carcinoma (HCC), a form of liver cancer. A recent study has attempted to improve the efficacy of ATO in treating solid tumours by combining it with N-(β-elemene-13-yl) tryptophan methyl ester (ETME).

The first study used human HCC cells in culture to assess the effects of ATO and ETME on cellular apoptosis. An initial study was performed which determined 20 μmol/l of ETME and 5 μmol/l of ATO should be used. HCC cells were seeded in a culture flask and exposed to ATO only, ETME only or a combination of both. After 48 hours, the cells were stained and cellular apoptosis was evaluated using a detection kit.

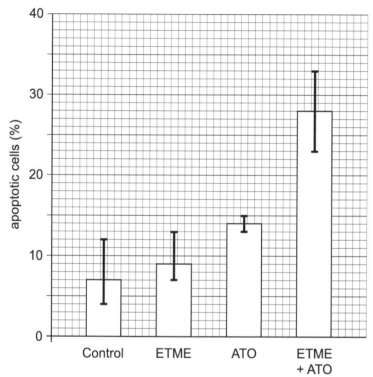

Figure 1: Effect of ETME and ATO on apoptosis of human HCC cells

Western blot analysis was performed to determine the effect of ETME, ATO and the combination on p53 protein expression in human HCC cells. After treatments, the cells were harvested and the protein within was isolated. The proteins were separated by electrophoresis and transferred to a membrane. The membrane was interrogated for the presence of p53 protein using an antibody linked to a reporter enzyme.

© HERIOT-WATT UNIVERSITY

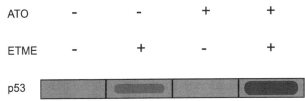

Figure 2: Blot showing the effect of ATO, ETME and the combination on the expression of p53 protein

A final study was conducted to determine the role of p53 in bringing about the apoptotic effect observed when ATO and ETME were used in combination. Human HCC cells were cultured as before with ATO, ETME or the combination. Cell samples from each treatment group were also exposed to a p53 inhibitor and the percentage of apoptotic cells was compared to those without the inhibitor.

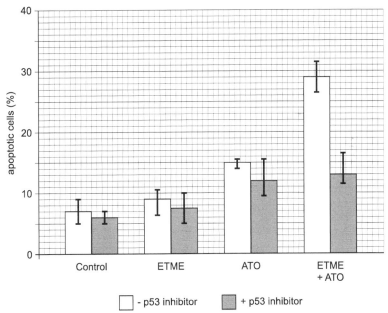

Figure 3: Effect of treatment with p53 inhibitor on apoptosis of human HCC cells

Q53: An initial study determined the concentrations of ATO and ETME which would be used in the main study. What name is given to an experiment which allows the development of protocols before the main study is undertaken? *(1 mark)*

....

Q54: Explain why the human HCC cells were left exposed to the compounds for 48 hours before the rate of apoptosis was assessed. *(1 mark)*

....

Q55: Figures 1 and 3 both show error bars. The error bars represent confidence intervals. What do the confidence intervals show about the data collected? *(1 mark)*

....

Q56: From Figure 1, it can be concluded that ATO and ETME together bring about a significant increase in the rate of apoptosis of human HCC cells in culture when compared to control cells or cells treated with ATO or ETME alone.
Explain how the error bars confirm that this conclusion is valid. *(2 marks)*

....

Q57: Use data from Figure 1 to show that the combination of ATO and ETME increased the rate of apoptosis by a factor of 4 when compared to the control. *(1 mark)*

....

Q58: It was concluded that ATO and ETME worked together to bring about apoptosis via a p53 dependent pathway.
How do the results from Figures 2 and 3 support this conclusion? *(2 marks)*

....

Q59: Further analysis showed that p53 activated a cascade of proteinases to bring about apoptosis. What term describes proteinases which bring about apoptosis? *(1 mark)*

....

....

Glossary

Active

a process which requires energy

Active site

the region of an enzyme molecule where the substrate binds

Apoptosis

programmed cell death

Archaea

one of the three domains of life, consisting of single celled microorganisms

ATP synthase

a membrane bound enzyme which generates ATP

Caspase

proteinases which destroy a cell

Centrifugation

a process which uses centrifugal forces to separate components of a mixture

Chromatography

a set of techniques which separates the components of a mixture

Colorimeter

a device that is used to measure the absorbance of a specific wavelength of light by a solution

Conformation

the spatial, or 3-D, arrangement of the atoms that make up the molecule

Depolarisation

an electrical state in an excitable cell whereby the inside of the cell is made less negative relative to the outside than at the resting membrane potential

Electrophoresis

a process which applies an electric current across a gel to separate components of a mixture

Eukaryotic

an organism which has a membrane bound nucleus

Extracellular

outside the cell

Fluorescence

the emission of light of a different wavelength to that which was absorbed

G-protein

proteins which act as molecular switches - they allow signals from outside the cell to be transmitted inside (they are involved in signal transduction); their activity is regulated by their ability to bind and break down GTP to GDP - when GTP is bound they are 'on' and when GDP is bound they are 'off'

Haemocytometer

a device used to count cells

Hybridoma

a cell formed from the fusion of a myeloma cell with an antibody-producing B-cell

Hydrophilic

(means 'water loving') a molecule of this type is electrically attracted to the polarity of the water molecules

Hydrophobic

(means 'water hating') a molecule of this type is not electrically attracted to the polarity of water and is repelled away from the water molecule

Hyperpolarisation

a change in a cell's membrane potential that makes it more negative

Immunoassay

techniques which use antibodies linked to reporter enzymes to cause a colour change in the presence of a specific antigen

Intracellular

inside the cell

Kinetochore

the point on a chromosome where the spindle fibre binds

Ligand

a substance which can bind to a protein

Lymphocyte

a type of white blood cell which forms part of the immune system

Monomer

a molecule that may bind chemically to other molecules to form a polymer

Myeloma

a B-cell cancer cell

Opsin

a photoreceptor molecule found in the animal kingdom

Passive

a process which does not require energy

Phagocyte

a type of white blood cell which engulfs and destroys foreign particles, bacteria or dead cells

Phosphorylation

the addition of a phosphate group to a molecule

Photon

a particle representing a quantum of light

Polymer

a large molecule, or macromolecule, composed of many repeated subunits, known as monomers

Polypeptide

a single chain of amino acids

Prosthetic group

a non-protein unit which is tightly bound to a protein that is necessary for its function

Proteinase

an enzyme which breaks down protein by hydrolysis

Proteolytic

substances which can break down proteins into smaller polypeptides or amino acids

Proton

a hydrogen ion

Retinal

a light-sensitive molecule

Standard curve

a graph which can be used to determine the concentration of an unknown solution

Symport

describes an integral membrane protein which is involved in simultaneously transporting two substances across the membrane in the same direction; in the case of glucose symport, glucose and sodium are simultaneously transported into cells

Thylakoid

a membrane-bound compartment found in chloroplasts, containing photosynthetic pigments

Answers to questions and activities

1 Laboratory techniques for biologists

Production of monoclonal antibodies (page 25)

Q1:

1. A laboratory animal is exposed to the antigen of interest.
2. B lymphocytes are removed from the spleen of the animal.
3. B lymphocytes are fused with myeloma cells using polyethylene glycol, forming hybridomas.
4. Individual hybridomas are cultured in a multiwell plate.
5. The culture medium can be removed and screened for the desired antibody.
6. Hybridomas which produce the desired antibody are cultured on a large scale.

End of Topic 1 test (page 39)

Q2:   Any two from:

- ensure that pregnant workers do not use it;
- wear gloves;
- wear a lab coat;
- have an established procedure for spills;
- maintain a clean working area before and after use;
- ensure that it is disposed of safely.

Q3:   Personal protective equipment

Q4:   To protect the body from harm.

Q5:   Any from:

- a lab coat;
- safety glasses;
- a face shield.

Q6:   To keep pH at a nearly constant value.

Q7:   Colorimeter

Q8:   600 μg/ml

Q9:   B lymphocytes

Q10: Hybridomas

Q11: PEG/polyethylene glycol

Q12: Serum

Q13: To prevent contamination.

Q14: Any from:

- wiping down surfaces with disinfectant;
- working in a cell culture hood;
- washing hands before and after a procedure;
- using sterile equipment.

Q15: Haemocytometer

2 Proteomics, protein structure, binding and conformational change

Extended response question: Structure of proteins (page 70)

Suggested marking scheme

Each line represents a point worth one mark. The concept may be expressed in other words. Words which are bracketed are not essential. Alternative answers are separated by a solidus (/); if both such answers are given, only a single mark is allocated. In checking the answer, the number of the point being allocated a mark should be written on the answer paper. A maximum of ten marks can be gained.

1. Primary structure of a protein is the sequence of amino acids in the polypeptide chain.

2. Amino acids are joined together by peptide bonds.

3. Secondary structure of a protein is stabilised by hydrogen bonds.

4. α-helix and β-sheet are two types of secondary structure.

5. α-helix is a spiral with the R groups sticking outwards.

6. β-sheet has parts of the chain running alongside each other forming a sheet.

7. The R groups sit above and below the sheet.

8. β-sheet can be anti-parallel or parallel.

9. Turns are a third type of secondary structure.

10. Tertiary structure refers to the final 3D structure of the protein.

11. Folding at this level is stabilised by many different interactions between the R groups of the amino acids.

12. Any two from: hydrophobic regions, ionic bonds, hydrogen bonds, van der Waals interactions, disulfide bridges.

13. Tertiary structure of a protein may include prosthetic (non-protein) parts.

14. For example, haem in haemoglobin.

15. Quaternary structure exists in proteins with several connected polypeptide subunits.

Extended response question: Enzyme activity (page 70)

Suggested marking scheme

Each line represents a point worth one mark. The concept may be expressed in other words. Words which are bracketed are not essential. Alternative answers are separated by a solidus (/); if both such answers are given, only a single mark is allocated. In checking the answer, the number of the point being allocated a mark should be written on the answer paper. A maximum of nine marks can be gained.

Induced fit *(maximum of 4 marks)*:

1. The active site is where a substrate binds to an enzyme.

2. The shape of the active site is specific/complementary to the substrate

3. When the correct substrate starts to bind, a temporary change in shape of the active site occurs.

4. The change in shape increases the binding and interaction with the substrate.

5. The chemical environment that is produced lowers the activation energy required for the reaction.

6. Once catalysis takes place, the original enzyme conformation is resumed.

Enzyme activation *(maximum of 5 marks)*:

i   Modulators change the rate of reaction/activity.

ii   Modulators bind at secondary binding sites.

iii Causes a conformation/shape change in the enzyme.

iv   Alters the affinity of the active site for the substrate.

v   Positive modulators increase the enzyme affinity for the substrate.

vi   Negative modulators reduce the enzyme's affinity for the substrate.

vii Phosphorylation/addition of a phosphate can alter enzyme activity.

viii Kinase enzymes carry out phosphorylation/adds phosphate.

End of Topic 2 test (page 71)

Q1: The entire set of proteins expressed by a genome.

Q2: The order in which the amino acids are synthesised into the polypeptide.

Q3: α-helix

Q4: Prosthetic group

Q5: Subunits

Q6: The R groups at the surface of a protein determine its location within a cell. **Hydrophilic** R groups will predominate at the surface of a soluble protein found in the cytoplasm.

Q7: In the soluble protein found in the cytoplasm, **hydrophobic** R groups may cluster at the centre to form a globular structure.

Q8: 1, 2 and 4

Q9: 3

Q10: Hydrophobic interactions

Q11: As a channel

Q12: A substance which can bind to a protein.

Q13: α-helix

Q14: The DNA backbone is negatively charged and the histone protein is positively charged.

Q15: Kinase

Q16: Phosphatase

Q17: ATPase

© HERIOT-WATT UNIVERSITY

3 Membrane proteins

Sodium-potassium pump (page 87)

Q1:

1. The transporter protein has high affinity for sodium ions inside the cell, therefore binding occurs.
2. Phosphorylation by ATP causes the conformation of the protein to change.
3. The affinity for ions changes, resulting in sodium being released outside of the cell.
4. Potassium ions from outside the cell bind to the sodium-potassium pump.
5. Dephosphorylation occurs, which causes the conformation of the protein to change.
6. Potassium ions are taken into the cell and the affinity returns to the start.

Extended response question: Movement of ions across membranes (page 94)

Suggested marking scheme

Each line represents a point worth one mark. The concept may be expressed in other words. Words which are bracketed are not essential. Alternative answers are separated by a solidus (/); if both such answers are given, only a single mark is allocated. In checking the answer, the number of the point being allocated a mark should be written on the answer paper. A maximum of ten marks can be gained.

Mechanism and functions of Na/K-ATPase *(maximum of 6 marks - any 4 from 1-6 and any 2 from 7-10)*:

1. Ions pumped against concentration gradient OR ions moved by active transport.

2. (3) sodium ions (pumped) out of cell and (2) potassium in.

3. Pump uses/hydrolyses ATP.

4. Phosphate attaches to protein or pump or Na/K-ATPase.

5. Phosphorylation alters conformation of protein.

6. (Different conformations) have different affinity for sodium and potassium.

7. The sodium-potassium pump is involved in maintaining the osmotic balance (in animal cells).

8. The sodium-potassium pump is involved in generating the ion gradient for glucose symport (in the small intestine).

9. The sodium-potassium pump is involved in generating and maintaining the ion gradient for resting potential in neurons.

10. The sodium-potassium pump is involved in generating an ion gradient in kidney tubules.

Nerve transmission *(maximum of 4 marks)*:

i   Resting potential across the plasma membrane.

ii   Ligand-gated channel opens to allow ions in.

iii Neurotransmitter is ligand.

iv   Ions enter and voltage (membrane potential) changes.

v   Voltage change opens voltage-gated channels (nearby).

vi   Sequence of voltage-gated channels open/wave of depolarisation.

End of Topic 3 test (page 95)

Q2:   Facilitated transport through transporter proteins is a **passive** process, meaning that it does not require energy.

Q3:   Some transporter proteins require energy to bring about the necessary conformational change. In this case the transport is **active**.

Q4:   Ligand-gated

Q5:   Signal transduction

Q6:   a) Potassium

Q7:   b) Sodium

Q8:   The sodium-potassium pump requires energy supplied by **ATP**.

Q9:   Phosphorylation changes the conformation/shape of the sodium-potassium pump/protein *(1 mark)* this changes the pump's/protein's affinity for ions. *(1 mark)*

Q10: 36,000

Q11: Membrane potential

Q12: Neurotransmitter

Q13: Voltage-gated

Q14: Nerve transmission is a wave of **depolarisation** of the resting potential of a neuron.

4 Detecting and amplifying an environmental stimulus

End of Topic 4 test (page 108)

Q1: Photoreceptor

Q2: d) Archaea, eukaryotes and prokaryotes

Q3: Bacteriorhodopsin molecules generate potential differences by absorbing light to pump **protons/hydrogen ions** across the membrane.

Q4: After being pumped across the membrane, they return through ATP **synthase**, generating ATP.

Q5: Absorption of light by photosynthetic pigments results in electrons being passed along a series of carrier proteins; this allows hydrogen ions to be pumped across the thylakoid membrane. Hydrogen ions then diffuse back across the membrane through ATP synthase, resulting in the production of ATP.

Q6: Opsin

Q7: Retinal

Q8: Rod

Q9: G-protein

5 Communication within multicellular organisms

Cell signalling: The action of testosterone (page 117)

Q1:

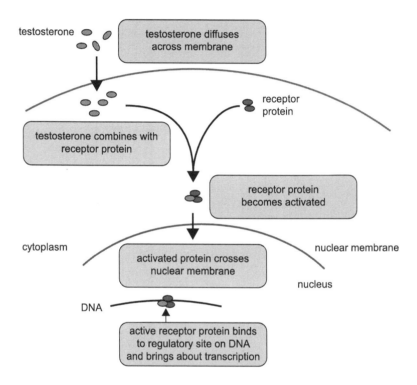

Extended response question: Cell signalling (page 127)

Suggested marking scheme

Each line represents a point worth one mark. The concept may be expressed in other words. Words which are bracketed are not essential. Alternative answers are separated by a solidus (/); if both such answers are given, only a single mark is allocated. In checking the answer, the number of the point being allocated a mark should be written on the answer paper. A maximum of eight marks can be gained.

1. Some signalling molecules/hormones are proteins/peptides/hydrophilic.

2. Hydrophilic/protein/peptide signalling molecules/hormones cannot cross the membrane.

3. The receptor for hydrophilic signals is in the membrane.

4. Binding changes the conformation of the receptor.

5. Receptors cause transduction/trigger cell response.

6. Example - insulin triggers recruitment of GLUT4/glucose transporters to the cell membrane OR ADH triggers recruitment of channel protein aquaporin 2 (AQP2).

7. Hydrophobic signals/steroid hormones/thyroxine can pass through the membrane.

8. The receptor for hydrophobic signals/steroid hormones is inside the cell/nucleus.

9. Protein/receptor is gene regulatory OR receptor-signal complex regulates transcription.

10. Example - thyroxine brings about transcription of gene for Na/KATPase OR steroid hormones/testosterone/oestrogen trigger transcription.

End of Topic 5 test (page 128)

Q2: a) The hormone thyroxine binds to a receptor protein on DNA and stops it inhibiting transcription.

Q3: In the cell OR in the nucleus.

Q4: Steroid OR hydrophobic hormones

Q5: On the cell surface OR on/in the membrane.

Q6: Collecting duct (of the kidney)

Q7: Aquaporin 2

Q8: Diabetes insipidus

Q9: Triggers recruitment of GLUT4 glucose transporters to the cell membrane of fat and muscle cells.

© HERIOT-WATT UNIVERSITY

6 Protein control of cell division

Mitosis (page 135)

Q1:

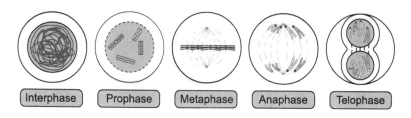

Interphase   Prophase   Metaphase   Anaphase   Telophase

Extended response question: Control of apoptosis (page 144)

Suggested marking scheme

Each line represents a point worth one mark. The concept may be expressed in other words. Words which are bracketed are not essential. Alternative answers are separated by a solidus (/); if both such answers are given, only a single mark is allocated. In checking the answer, the number of the point being allocated a mark should be written on the answer paper. A maximum of eight marks can be gained.

1. Destruction of cells/apoptosis/programmed cell death must be carefully controlled in a multicellular organism.

2. Programmed cell death/apoptosis is triggered by cell death signals.

3. These signals activate inactive forms of DNAase and proteinases that destroy the cell.

4. The proteinases are known as caspases.

5. Cell death signals may originate outwith the cell/may be extrinsic.

6. For example lymphocytes.

7. The signal binds to a surface receptor protein.

8. Binding activates a protein cascade that produces active caspases/proteinases.

9. Death signals may also originate within the cell/may be intrinsic.

10. For example DNA damage.

11. DNA damage triggers the activation of p53 protein.

12. The presence of p53 protein can activate a caspase cascade.

13. In the absence of cell growth factors, cells may also initiate apoptosis.

© HERIOT-WATT UNIVERSITY

End of Topic 6 test (page 144)

Q2: d) protein.

Q3: All eukaryotic cells have microtubules. These are hollow rods constructed of columns of a protein called **tubulin**.

Q4: In animal cells, microtubules radiate out from a region near the nucleus called the **centrosome**.

Q5: b) M, G1, S, G2

Q6: a) Anaphase

Q7: c) Prophase

Q8: b) Metaphase

Q9: d) Telophase

Q10: d) undergo chromosomal duplication.

Q11: a) G1

Q12: Causes phosphorylation of proteins (that stimulate the cell cycle).

Q13: p53

Q14: Caspases

Q15: DNA damage OR absence of cell growth factors.

Q16: Any from:

- degenerative conditions;
- organ/tissue formation (during development);
- tumour formation.

7 End of unit test

End of Unit 1 test (page 150)

Q1: Personal protective equipment

Q2: A colorimeter

Q3: 800

Q4: B lymphocytes and myeloma.

Q5: Using a reporter enzyme (linked to the antibody) which causes a colour change.

Q6: To count the number of cells in a solution to find the concentration.

Q7: Serum

Q8: To prevent contamination.

Q9: Proteome

Q10: Peptide

Q11: Hydrogen

Q12: α-helix

Q13: Prosthetic group

Q14: The R groups at the surface of a protein.

Q15: Strong hydrophobic interactions hold **integral** proteins within the phospholipid bilayer.

Q16: Peripheral proteins have fewer hydrophobic R groups interacting with the phospholipids.

Q17: The DNA backbone is negatively charged and the histone protein is positively charged.

Q18: When the correct substrate starts to bind, a temporary change in shape of the active site occurs increasing the binding and interaction with the substrate.

Q19: Cooperativity

Q20: Kinase

Q21: Passive

Q22: Conformational change in active transport requires energy from hydrolysis of **ATP**.

Q23: Voltage-gated

© HERIOT-WATT UNIVERSITY

Q24: Any from:

- activation of an enzyme;
- activation of a G-protein;
- a change in uptake or secretion of molecules;
- rearrangement of the cytoskeleton;
- activation of proteins that regulate gene transcription.

Q25: a) Generation of adenosine triphosphate (ATP).

Q26: b) Three sodium ions out of the cell, two potassium ions into the cell.

Q27: Nerve transmission is a wave of **depolarisation** of the resting potential of a neuron.

Q28: A signal molecule/neurotransmitter triggers the opening of ligand-gated ion channels. *(1 mark)*
If sufficient ion movement occurs, then voltage-gated ion channels will open. *(1 mark)*
This triggers a sequence of voltage-gated channels to open/a wave of depolarisation. *(1 mark)*

Q29: Hydrogen

Q30: ATP synthase

Q31: Retinal

Q32: Any from:

- activation of G-proteins;
- activation of enzymes;
- ion channels close;
- hyperpolarisation of the membrane.

Q33: a) Cone cells do not function in low light intensity and contain different forms of opsins.

Q34: It changes conformation/shape.

Q35: Hydrophobic signalling molecules can pass across the membrane.

Q36: b) Thyroxine brings about transcription of the gene for Na/K-ATPase.

Q37: Transcription factors

Q38: Any from:

- loss of insulin receptor function/sensitivity;
- insulin receptor fails to function;
- insulin receptor does not respond to insulin.

Q39: It triggers recruitment of GLUT4/glucose transporters so can improve uptake of glucose to fat and muscle cells.

Q40: It triggers recruitment of channel protein aquaporin 2/AQP2 to the cell membrane.

Q41: Diabetes insipidus

Q42: b) S

Q43: Degenerative

Q44: b) Metaphase

Q45: d) Telophase

Q46: c) Prophase

Q47: a) Anaphase

Q48: a) DNA replication to occur.

Q49: Spindle fibres

Q50: They cause phosphorylation of proteins that stimulate the cell cycle.

Q51: Any from:

- stimulate DNA repair;
- stop the cell cycle;
- cause cell death/apoptosis.

Q52: DNA damage

Q53: Pilot study

Q54: To allow the chemicals/compounds to have an effect OR to allow apoptosis to begin.

Q55: Variability around the average/mean result.

Q56: Error bars do not overlap so differences (between rates of apoptosis) are significant/rates (of apoptosis) could not be the same.

Q57: The average percentage of apoptotic cells in the control is 7 and in the presence of ATO and ETME the average percentage of apoptotic cells 28, which is a difference of four times.

Q58: Western blot analysis shows that p53 protein expression is up-regulated/increased when cells are treated with the combination of ATO and ETME. *(1 mark)*
When a p53 inhibitor is present the apoptotic effect of ATO and ETME is reversed/reduced. *(1 mark)*

Q59: Caspase